Ferguson, MO
What Really Happened
A Systematic, Scientific Analysis

Front Cover Image

Extracted from Grand Jury Evidence
Ferguson PD Crime Scene Photo
Photo Number 74780014

Author Contact Information

Bruce Krell, PhD
www.shooters-edge.com

bruce@shooters-edge.com

Ferguson, MO
What Really Happened
A Systematic, Scientific Analysis

Get the Edge

BRUCE E. KRELL, PHD
SHOOTERS-EDGE, INC

ISBN: 0-9966250-0-3
ISBN 13: 978-0-9966250-0-5

Library of Congress Control Number: 2015914166
Shooters-Edge, Inc., Los Angeles, CA

Printed in the United States
CreateSpace Independent Publishing Platform
                North Charleston, South Carolina

First Edition: 2015

Dedication

<u>To My Brother</u>

Rick Krell

Your Life Was Way Too Short But You Gave A Lot To All Of Us

<u>To My Father-In-Law</u>

Iwaichi Muto

Thanks For Giving Me My Better Half, Your Daughter Michiko

To The Reader

Using a systematic and scientific analysis of the shooting incident in Ferguson, MO, on August 9, 2014, this book clearly demonstrates:

- Michael Brown was charging Officer Darren Wilson

- Wilson was retreating, discharging his firearm in order to defend himself.

- Wilson was in fear for his life because Brown charging constituted a deadly weapon.

I DID NOT BEGIN WITH THESE RESULTS.

I started with the Grand Jury evidence. After analyzing this evidence, I performed evidence collection experiments. I then systematically combined aspects of the evidence, the experiments, and math, science, and physics to reach those conclusions.

Using this approach, I **OBJECTIVELY** evaluated multiple theories of the incident to determine the above conclusions as the only scientifically reasonable theory of the incident. Moreover, I performed this analysis in a repeatable way, listing the steps I followed in order to evaluate each theory of the incident.

NO ONE ASKED ME TO DO THIS ANALYSIS.

I performed this analysis completely on my own and at my own expense. I simply wanted to use my special knowledge, skills, experience, education and training to understand this incident.

Acknowledgements

A large number of people have contributed to honing the skills and expertise that enabled the analysis included in this book:

Michiko Krell, my wife, who believes that I can accomplish anything that I attempt, seems unperturbed by my changes in profession, and still declares that I am not usable around the house.

Judge Henry Hall, LA County Superior Court, head of the Expert Witness Panel, for keeping me on the panel.

judges, prosecutors, and defense attorneys with whom I have interacted over the years who, for the most part, have been seekers of the truth, very professional, and a credit to the American judicial system, Thanks to all of you for the experiences that you have provided.

members of the various crime labs with whom I have interacted have also, for the most part, been very professional, and again, a credit to the American judicial system.

detectives and sworn officers of the various law enforcement agencies, with whom I have interacted, and who generally as a group, want to serve the community and to make the world a better place to live.

Dr. Jack Mogg, my dissertation advisor at the University of Houston, and lifelong friend until his passing, who set the foundation for my analytical skills that have served me throughout my career.

Dr. Jon Collins, Acta, Inc., my mentor in the area of trajectory physics and ballistics, and lifelong friend until his passing, who provided the research and practical experience in ballistics.

Sgt Major William Skiles, USMC (Ret), who invited me to be the Ballistics Instructor at the Marine Sniper School, Camp Pendleton, CA, enabling me to learn a huge amount regarding practical aspects of ballistic physics.

Anna Mueller, Deputy Public Defender, LA County Public Defender's Office, who encouraged me to develop "Attorney Firearms Training", a continuing education course certified by the CA Bar Association, that initiated my career as an expert witness.

Joan Croker, Head Deputy, LA County Public Defender's Office, who also encouraged me to become involved as an expert witness and takes great pleasure in reminding me of my initial reluctance.

Chuck Michel and Joe Silvoso, the best firearms attorneys around, who work very hard to protect the gun rights of us ordinary citizens.

Michael Olecki, Grodsky & Olecki, litigating attorney, who gave me an intense, hands-on, 40 hour training session many years ago on how to testify as an expert witness.

Mark Nelson, PhD, Princeton, Physics, who reviewed a draft of this book, performed quality checks, and provided substantive comments to improve the readability of the book.

David Shur and Kyle Russell, who represented Wilson and Brown in the visual reconstructions.

Table Of Contents

Commentary

Wisely and slow. They stumble that run fast.

Romeo and Juliet, Act II, Scene iii, William Shakespeare

I am always surprised at how some people want to rush to judgment without allowing both prosecution and defense to examine and investigate. Some residents of Ferguson, MO, and the aftermath in the community, are perfect examples of this rush to judgment.

When the community or members of the judicial system rush to judgment, the whole judicial system stumbles. A miscarriage of justice is usually the result. Justice is better served by moving wisely and slowly so that the truth will out.

O judgment, thou art fled to brutish beasts,

And men have lost their reason!

Julius Caesar, Act III, Scene ii, William Shakespeare

There is no greater evil than anarchy.

Antigone, Sophocles, 442 BCE

Uninformed residents and outside agitators who did not like the result of the Grand Jury verdict used the verdict to act like beasts and to commit extensive property damage. Regardless of the race or color of the perpetrator, this type of violent behavior without judgment is anarchy. Destructive anarchy without justification, seems to be growing and growing and is pure evil. Innocent people and businesses are hurt. In the end, the community suffers because businesses will not take the risk of operating in the community.

Preface

I reconstruct shooting incidents.

Well, among other activities as an expert witness, I do. At the time of this writing, I have had 150 or so cases, at least 75 involving detailed shooting incident reconstructions. I have testified on shooting incidents in 10-12 of these 75 cases. In these shooting incidents, I have sided with the defense about 70% of the time and with the prosecution about 30% of the time. My reconstruction of a shooting incident results in a report that generally consists of 40-100 heavily annotated slides with lots of math, physics, photos, and often pictures or videos with actors portraying events and highlighting issues. I am very thorough, period.

Over the years, I have had a number of careers. I started my career as an Applied Mathematician. Then, I become a System Engineer. After a while, I transitioned to being a Software Architect/Computer Scientist. Finally, I returned to my real love, applied mathematics and applied physics.

During those periods, I simultaneously worked in a number of other areas -- such as ballistics and applied physics. I developed my first ballistics trajectory program in 1977. I taught ballistics for the Marine Sniper School at Camp Pendleton, as a civilian instructor, from about 2000 - 2002. My pay was to take the training, which I did at age 50. I developed the first ballistic trajectory programs for a handheld computer, MOAMaster, for which I hold a registered copyright. I worked and taught courses in image processing and sound analysis. And, I have spent the last five years as a licensed gunsmith/firearms dealer, where I have repaired and modified hundreds of firearms of all types. I also have been a very active firearms instructor for 17 years now.

Four areas of extensive experience as both a **practitioner and instructor** have provided the basis for my skills to perform shooting incident reconstruction: applied mathematics/applied physics, trajectory ballistics, gunsmith/firearms instructor, and systems engineer.

Applied mathematics is the basis for all science and engineering. As an applied mathematician, I have a very analytical, rigorous mind. In other words, I **can see through the nonsense** and see all the gaping holes in any set of evidence. As an applied mathematician, I have always had a keen interest in applied physics and various areas of engineering, where I have worked over the years. After all, physics and engineering are simply branches of applied math specifically oriented towards predicting solutions to real problems.

One of the more interesting areas of applied physics is trajectory physics. The mathematical models for trajectories are extensions of the work by Sir Isaac Newton, back in the mid 1700s. As a licensed gunsmith, I have a detailed, practical hands-on knowledge of how a large number of firearms work. I regularly take apart guns for repair/modification. Diagnosing and fixing a broken firearm involves understanding how the parts of the firearm interact.

Shooting incident reconstruction is based upon trajectory physics and firearms operations. So, the combination of applied math, applied physics, trajectory ballistics, firearms parts interactions in my background provide a strong scientific basis for performing shooting incident reconstruction.

But, perhaps, the strongest basis for my expertise to perform shooting incident reconstructions comes from my almost 40 years of experience as a systems engineer. Systems engineers look at all the parts of system, how these parts interact to perform the job of the system. Shooting reconstruction uses the exact same principles. When a shooting incident reconstruction is performed, interaction of a number of elements must be understood. Trajectory physics/ballistics, firearms operations/ejection patterns, physical evidence, such as bullet wound paths, location of fired casings, location of blood droppings at the scene, location of a body, and witness statements all must be taken into account and integrated into a consistent explanation of who, what, when, where, and how.

After all, the shooting incident is in fact a "system." The components of the system are all the elements described above. Interaction of these elements in a **LOGICAL, CONSISTENT** manner reveal the truth of what happened in an incident. So, many of the skills, techniques, and analytical approaches used to perform system engineering apply to shooting incident reconstruction.

My goal at the start of and during any shooting incident reconstruction is to seek the truth. I am objective. I evaluate based on the evidence outlined above. Whenever I make conclusions, I back them to the hilt with science, math, physics, and evidence. So, I did **NOT** start out with the intention to prove the conclusions in this book. The same evidence that was presented to the Grand Jury, along with some experiments I performed, some reconstruction with actors, and my own analyses, led me to those conclusions.

And, lest you think that I am biased in any way, please return to the first paragraph on page 1 and reread my record. I am brutally critical with lots of support for my positions, as any of the prosecutors or defense attorneys with whom I have interacted will be happy to tell you.

This Ferguson case is the perfect example of a shooting incident reconstruction. All of the elements outlined above are in play.

I have several goals in writing this book:

- identify the scientific basis of shooting incident reconstruction

- define a systematic approach for performing a reconstruction

- provide a practical example of the reconstruction process

- give insight into how I actually think about various elements of a shooting incident

- determine what really happened between Officer Darren Wilson and Michael Brown in Ferguson, MO, on August 9, 2014.

- provide a technical reference for other practitioners who want to systematically perform a shooting incident reconstruction

- provide a readable, understandable, common sense experience in shooting reconstructions for those persons not in the law enforcement industry.

Buckle up and enjoy the ride.

Bruce E. Krell, PhD   Los Angeles, CA   July, 2015

A Note About Sources

Most of the information in this book comes from a small number of sources, which are generally identified at the time of usage.

The Grand Jury Documents And Photos

Made Public By

Robert McCulloch, Prosecutor, St. Louis County, MO

Original Materials And Annotations

Created By

Bruce E. Krell, PhD, Shooters - Edge, Inc.

Head Renderings

Used With Permission

Sergey Strelkov, Asst Professor
St. Petersburg State Polytechnic University, Russia

Ferguson, MO In A Nutshell

This book provides a systematic and scientific analysis of the shooting incident in Ferguson, MO on August 9, 2014. A **simple, clear, precise summary** of the analysis results appears below.

- The wound path from the top of the head, vertically downward through the body, caused Brown's death.
- A wound path through the top of the head, vertically downward, occurs if the upper body is parallel to the ground.
- Brown's upper body was parallel to the ground only if **BROWN WAS CHARGING**.
- Wilson's Sig Sauer P-229 pistol with similar ammunition had an ejection pattern that was 8' at the base and 13' at the centerline.
- The fired casing area after the incident covered a distance of about 24' along its widest edge.
- A minimum of three (3) of the P-229 8' ejection pattern areas fit within the fired casing area.
- Since multiple ejection pattern areas fit within the fired casing area, **WILSON WAS RETREATING AND SHOOTING**.
- Dr. Michael Baden described a body position from the wound paths that **CORROBORATES** Brown charging.
- Brown's **CHARGING IMPACT FORCE** is equivalent to the impact force of a 40 pound rock swung at 40 miles/hour.

Michael Brown was charging.

Officer Wilson was retreating, shooting to defend himself.

Introduction

On November 24, 2014, Prosecuting Attorney Robert McColluch announced the decision of the Grand Jury in the shooting death of Michael Brown. The jury declined to indict Officer Darren Wilson for the shooting of Michael Brown on August 9, 2014.

Most of the documents and images submitted to the Grand Jury were placed on line for public review and evaluation. An extensive review of these documents reveals that no one attempted to reconstruct the shooting incident in a systematic way, starting with the wound paths described in the autopsy reports by both the St. Louis County Medical Examiner and Dr. Michael Baden, the independent medical examiner.

A Systematic And Scientific Approach To Reconstruction

This book establishes and demonstrates a systematic approach for performing shooting incident reconstruction, based on trajectory physics and ejection patterns, along with the Medical Examiner's report, physical evidence, and eyewitness testimony. Principles and techniques are illustrated as the basis for reconstruction of a shooting incident. These techniques include geometry, dowels and wound path reconstruction, bullet path reconstruction, consideration of alternative theories of the incident, and corroboration with witness statements and other evidence. Little, if any, detailed medical knowledge is necessary, because the wound specifications are pretty much basic high school geometry and high school biology.

This systematic approach, combined with the principles, procedures, and techniques, is used with the Medical Examiner's report and other corroborating evidence to evaluate the incident in which Officer Wilson shot Michael Brown. Analysis clearly shows that based on the bullet path in the Medical Examiner's report and corroborated with science, physics, the physical evidence and other corroborating evidence, Michael Brown was indeed charging Officer Darren Wilson, not surrendering with his hands in the air. Furthermore, Officer Wilson was in retreat, shooting in defense at the charging Michael Brown.

Based on this analysis, the Grand Jury came to the right conclusion! Darren Wilson was defending himself, not executing Michael Brown.

Conditions For The Systematic Analysis

The systematic analysis performed in this book focuses on a very specific period of the interaction between Officer Wilson and Michael Brown.

Prior to this portion of the incident, a struggle between Wilson and Brown had taken place. Wilson was in his vehicle. Brown was leaning into the vehicle. Brown was attempting to obtain possession of the Wilson's firearm.

After this struggle, Brown started to walk away. Wilson exited his police vehicle and followed. Wilson thought that Brown might have been a suspect in a recent holdup and so shouted for Brown to surrender.

At this point, the systematic analysis begins.

After some as yet unspecified sequence of events, Michael Brown lay dead on the ground.

At this point, the systematic analysis ends.

<u>At best, this event was not more than about 10 seconds long.</u>

So, the primary goal is to use a systematic and scientific approach to answer a very specific question: what really happened between the time that Wilson asked Brown to surrender and the time that Brown was found dead on his stomach on the ground.

Grand Jury Evidence Released To The Public

After Robert McCulloch announced the decision of the Grand Jury, he very quickly announced that most of the evidence submitted to the Grand Jury would be made publically available.

As you might guess, this announcement made me very excited. I performed a Google search and found the documents on line. In fear that McCulloch might catch so much grief that he would change his mind and withdraw the documents, I immediately downloaded all of the documents and all of the evidence photos.

After getting all the documents and photos onto my hard drive, I performed a summary of the evidence.

Category	Document Count
Grand Jury Transcripts	27
Forensic And Other Reports	23
Witness Interviews	55
Photos	254

Table 1: Grand Jury Evidence Summary

I thought that I had died and gone to heaven. Robert McCulloch seemed to have kept his word.

This complete set of evidence amounted to thousands of pages of documentation, a large chore for anyone to evaluate.

In order to perform a reconstruction, you absolutely **MUST** review all of the evidence. Do **NOT** let anyone filter the evidence for you. If someone else attempts to give you a subset of the information, you may miss an important fact or a key piece of information. **You and you alone must decide the elements of the evidence that are important to your reconstruction.**

If someone else deletes a critical piece of information, the absence of this information can result in false conclusions. Finding out during cross examination that your systematic evaluation is flawed because you are confronted with a key piece of information that contradicts your analysis is embarrassing and unprofessional.

A Summary Of The Systematic, Scientific Analysis

The analysis presented in this book is very detailed and very thorough and spread throughout a large number of pages.. This chapter **collects all of the spread out, relevant information into a single location,** providing a detailed summary of the analysis that was performed.

Grand Jury Evidence

- Wilson was 210 pounds; Brown was 289 pounds.

- Darren Wilson carried a Sig Sauer P-229 pistol chambered in caliber 40 Smith & Wesson.

- Darren Wilson utilized Federal cartridges with bullet weights ranging from 158 - 180 grains.

- The key wound paths started in the top of the head.

- The key wound paths proceeded downward through the body.

- No soot or stippling was found at the entrance of any of the wounds.

- Dorian Johnson, the percipient witness, claims that Brown was shot just after turning .

- Other witness statements cover a wide range of possible theories.

Scientific Basis

- Bullet trajectory is practically flat and straight for the first 25 yards, regardless of the caliber.

- Ejection pattern forms a triangle that is characterized by direction/angle, distance, and width.

- The system of a shooting incident has 4 components -- straight and flat trajectory, shooter position, ejection distance, and ejection direction.

- Momentum can be used to compare the ability of two objects to stay on the same straight flat path prior to impact.

- Force can be used to compare the effect of various impacting objects on an impacted object.

- An entry wound and exit wound body path description is the two point specification of a line in simple geometry.

- An entry wound and impact angle body path description is the point angle specification of a line in simple geometry.

Initial Examination Evidence

- Brown moved 21' 7" from the turning location to the final position of his body on the ground.

- Wilson moved 22' 8" from when Brown turned towards Wilson to the end of the incident

Experimental Evidence

- A Sig P-229 with similar ammo used has an ejection pattern with an ejection direction of 125° and an ejection distance of 13'.

- A Sig P-229 with similar ammo used has an ejection pattern that covers a triangle 8' wide at the base and 13' high at the centerline.

- With Wilson's pistol and similar ammunition, almost all of the soot and all of the stippling has disappeared when the muzzle is about 8' from the target.

Systematic And Scientific Analysis

- Head wound path one (1), through the top of the head and vertically downward through the head, was the wound path that terminated the life of Brown.

- Since the line of sight, the trajectory bullet path and the wound bullet path perfectly coincide for head wound path one (1) when Brown is charging, Brown charging is scientifically correct and is exactly what happened.

- Brown charging is the only scientifically correct theory of the incident because this theory was the only theory in which the line of sight, the trajectory bullet path and the wound bullet path perfectly coincide for head wound path one (1) .

- Wilson was retreating while shooting. This movement is explained by the multiple ejection pattern areas inside the fired casing area and by the resultant multiple shooting positions.

- Since the chest wound path angle and the bullet trajectory path

15

angles relative to the vertical axis of the body do not match, Brown could not have been standing during the time at which the chest wound path was created.

- Time had passed between the witness hearing shots in the residence and the witness standing at the observation location. Given this time delay, the statement by this witness that Brown was on his knees has no evidentiary value.

- If Brown had been shot by Wilson just after turning, the chest wound path would have passed straight through the upper body. Since the chest wound path angled downward, Johnson's description of the conditions under which Wilson shot Brown are not scientifically possible.

- Dr. Michael Baden, independent Medical Examiner, describes Brown in a charging body position when the bullet paths were created

- Brown's force at impact is equivalent to the impact force of a 40 pound rock swung at 40 miles/hour.

- If a charging Brown had impacted Wilson, some damage and potentially the death of Wilson would have occurred.

- Standing/surrendering starts with a potential weight imbalance to the rearward, resulting in a final resting position with the back on the ground and palms face down.

- This final, resting position of Brown's body does not match Brown's actual final, resting position on the ground.

- Charging starts with a potential weight imbalance to the

forward, resulting in a final resting position with the stomach on the ground and palms face up.

- This final, resting position of Brown's body does match Brown's actual final, resting position on the ground.

<u>**Michael Brown was charging.**</u>
<u>**Officer Wilson was retreating, shooting to defend himself.**</u>

These statements are all conclusions concerning the evaluation of the evidence using the system and scientific approach.

Conclusions are not valid without proof as to the manner in which the conclusions were reached.

Please read the remainder of the this book to see how these conclusions were obtained.

Sifting Through The Grand Jury Evidence

I spent many hours poring over the Grand Jury evidence. After all of my experience with shooting incident cases, I have a specific order in which I searched through the evidence.

Principles Of Evidence Extraction

Initially, I found the specific date, time, and **location of the incident** as well as a summary of the **sequence of events**. The physical layout of the area at the scene often contains indicators that give insight into evaluation of the sequence of events. Location may also raise line of sight issues. In a local incident, I would go out to the physical location with a camera and take lots of pictures from lots of angles, at locations indicated by the sequence of events. In this case, travel was not feasible, so I studied the physical environment of the incident using Google Earth. Date and time are important, because the lighting conditions may contradict statements by witnesses.

After the location and sequence, I found the **physical characteristics of the participants**. Often in an incident, one party may have leverage over the other party, which shapes the evaluation of the interaction. Relative heights and weights of the participants generally reveal which participant has the leverage or control over the situation.

Next, I found a drawing by the crime scene team indicating the **map and locations of fired casings and other physical evidence**. Fired casing locations help to locate the position of the shooter and provide indicators as to whether the shooter was standing still or moving. Locations of blood markers and bodies can also tell whether the victims were moving and the direction of movement.

The next piece of evidence that I found was the manufacturer and model of the **firearm** used by Officer Wilson and the type of **ammunition** employed. These two pieces of information are used to specifically determine the ejection pattern of the firearm, one of the core elements of the scientific foundation of the systematic approach.

The next topic of interest is the **wounds and the wound paths**. I found the **Medical Examiner's Reports**. I was interested in the report by the St. Louis County Medical Examiner and the report by Dr. Michael Baden, the independent medical examiner hired by the Brown family. I wanted to know about any similarities, any differences, and any conclusions that may have been made from either about the position of the body.

A key piece of evidence is all of the **police investigation reports**. These reports were easily located within the Grand Jury evidence. Police reports are a great summary of all of the evidence and the alleged sequence of events. An investigation report also often describes the position of the body at the time of the examination. Body position at death can be used to determine the position of the body just prior to death. In this case, body position will help determine Brown's actions before death. *Great care needs to be taken when evaluating these reports. These reports are often biased towards interpreting the evidence in a manner that supports a specific theory of the crime.* When reviewing these reports, take care to extract true facts and not facts biased by a particular theory of the events. Isolating the key elements of the included sequence of events also serves as a basis for identifying alternate theories of the incident. Use the incident report information to identify alternate theories of the incident and not as fact.

Finally, **witness statements** have to be reviewed. Witness statements can either corroborate or contradict both the scientific elements or the physical evidence.

In this case, two specific categories of statements were considered.

Dorian Johnson, the friend of Michael Brown who was **the most percipient witness**, made some very clear claims that needed to be understood. A percipient witness is a witness who testifies about something he or she claims to have actually seen. Much of the media seemed to give huge credibility to the statements by Dorian Johnson, just because of his position as the most percipient witness. But, that belief simply may not be correct in the face of the scientific or physical evidence.

Statements made by **other witnesses** needed to be categorized and understood. Categorization and summary are extremely important. In most cases with multiple witnesses, the witness statements are generally all over the place. Given the number of witness interviews and testimony presented to the Grand Jury, the witnesses were all over the place. So, placing the witnesses in categories identifies the general behavior observed by groups of witnesses. Evaluation of the witness testimony in concert with the scientific and physical evidence can then focus on the behaviors in the categories. Examples of behaviors include surrendering, charging, kneeling, sitting, on the ground, etc.

Summary Of The Evidence Extraction Sequence

In summary, the following evidence needs to be extracted from the overall stack of evidence to provide a basis for the systematic reconstruction of a shooting incident reconstruction when a person is shot:

- location of the incident

- summary of sequence of events

- physical characteristics of the participants

- map and locations of fired casings and physical evidence

- firearms and ammunition involved

- wounds and wound paths

- police investigation reports

- statements of percipient witnesses

- statements of other witnesses

All of this data was available in the Grand Jury evidence released to the public.

Furthermore, a quick glance at the extracted evidence informed me that the content and format were sufficiently organized and detailed as to allow me to perform a systematic reconstruction.

Evidence In This Case Compared With Other Cases

The list of evidence items in this case does not constitute a complete list or even a list appropriate for every shooting incident.

Shooting incidents cover a wide range of scenarios and conditions. For other scenarios, other types of evidence may be appropriate. Evidence in some incidents may include surveillance video, audio recordings, bullets from bodies, fired casings found at the scene of the incident, discovered hidden firearms, dropped firearms, bullet impact characterizations (height, angles left/right and up/down), and a large range of other items.

While all of the necessary evidence seems to be available in this case, the existence, format and content of that necessary evidence may be a mixed bag in other cases. In these shooting incidents, I never seem to get the exact same data to the exact same level of detail, even if the crime scene analysts are from the same crime lab and have undergone the same training.

In other cases, some of this evidence may not even be available or may be available in other forms, or may not be specific enough for systematic reconstruction.

For instance, wounds and wound paths may not be available if no Medical Examiner's reports are involved. However, if Medical Examiner's reports aren't involved, crime scene teams usually provide bullet impact characterizations -- height above the ground and impact angles -- up/down and left/right. From this information, a bullet path can be constructed using reverse trajectory analysis, either with dowels through the air or tapes on the ground replicating the ground path.

23

If the victim was only wounded and then treated by an emergency room doctor, then the wound information is often less than satisfactory. For instance, an emergency room doctor may indicate the number of bullet wounds without exactly specifying which wounds are entrances, which wounds are exits, and which entrances and exits combine to form bullet paths. In this situation, an independent pathologist should be consulted to prepare the diagrams which identify this information from the medical reports.

Most case reports also contain extensive property reports. These reports carefully detail the location where any piece of physical evidence is found, a careful description of the evidence item, and usually the condition of the evidence item.

These reports should be carefully studied. In some cases, the location at which an evidence item is found can make a difference in the theory of the incident. For instance, if a shooter is aiming in a specific direction, using a firearm that ejects to the right, and standing in the middle of a street, casings found on the left side of the shooter at a great distance did not come from the firearm of the shooter.

Condition of evidence items can also play a significant role in the reconstruction process. Fired casings found fifteen minutes after an incident that are crushed and corroded also did not have anything to do with the incident. Crushing indicates that the casings had been run over by vehicles. Corrosion indicates that the casings had been on site for a long time, subjected to rain. Recently fired casings are generally bright and shiny.

None of these has any bearing to the incident under analysis here. The Grand Jury evidence released to the public had almost everything necessary to perform the reconstruction, except some specific evidence that needed to be empirically collected by experiment.

Grand Jury Evidence Summary

For purposes of reconstruction, the evidence extracted from the Grand Jury evidence is first evaluated. This evidence consists of pretty much everything except the eye-witness statements. These statements will be summarized and evaluated during the corroboration phase of reconstruction.

Location and Sequence Of Events

The Grand Jury evidence provided an aerial view of the location of the incident location.

Figure 1: Aerial View, Location of the Incident

Although not source identified in the extracted evidence, this view was provided by Google Earth. In fact, the actual evidence included a broader aerial view. This crop from the aerial view was selected in order to focus attention on the actual location of the incident.

The shooting incident occurred in the 2940 - 2960 block of Canfield Drive, in Ferguson, MO. Other streets involved in the sequence of events include Copper Creek Court to the upper right of the view and Caddlefield Road towards the bottom of the view.

Studying the actual police reports, more specific information is available as to location and the sequence of events.

Figure 2: Annotated Aerial View

Reviewing some of the evidence materials, such as the police reports and location maps, a reasonable sequence of actions can be constructed. The locations of the sequence of actions were not part of the Grand Jury evidence but have been annotated onto the aerial view.

1: Officer Wilson is in his vehicle on Canfield Drive. Brown leans into the vehicle and attempts to take possession of the Wilson's pistol. The pistol discharges. Brown receives a wound in the hand and possibly in the upper arm. Wilson exhibits rough, red areas on his face and head as a result of the altercation.

2: Michael Brown and his friend Dorian Johnson turn and begin to walk down Canfield Drive away from Officer Wilson's vehicle towards Copper Creek Court.

3: Officer Wilson exits his vehicle and walks down Canfield Drive towards Copper Creek Court. Wilson shouts for Brown and Johnson to halt. Brown turns towards Officer Wilson. Johnson moves over to the other side of the street, out of the way.

A short time later after turning towards Officer Wilson, Michael Brown lay face down on Canfield Drive.

**THE GOAL OF THIS BOOK IS TO UNDERSTAND EXACTLY WHAT HAPPENED BETWEEN THE TIME THAT BROWN TURNED TOWARDS OFFICER WILSON AND THE TIME THAT BROWN LAY FACE DOWN ON THE GROUND.**

According to Google Earth, the distance between the location of Wilson's vehicle and the location where Brown turned to face Officer Wilson is about 50 yards. This distance is a fairly short distance, about 1/2 of a football field.

This shortness is important because some people claim that Wilson chased Brown for a couple of blocks, indicating an intent for revenge. The pursuit was at most 50 yards, maybe less, not a couple of blocks. The issue of intent for revenge just does not make sense at this short of a distance.

Physical Characteristics of the Participants

Clearly from the earlier discussion, only two participants in the incident are of interest: Officer Darren Wilson and Michael Brown.

Darren Wilson is the police officer involved in the incident.

Figure 3: Officer Darren Wilson
Source: Grand Jury Evidence Released

Officer Wilson is 6' 4" in height, weighing in at 210 pounds.

Michael Brown is the civilian involved in the incident.

Figure 4: Michael Brown
Source: Dozens of Web Sites

Michael Brown was 6' 5" in height, weighing 289 pounds.

This comparison is important. Both the participants were the same approximate height. This fact provides some initial insight to the possible positions of both participants at the time of the shooting.

If the bullet path is from the chest to the back and parallel to the ground, then both participants could have been standing. This situation could **POSSIBLY** indicate that Michael Brown was surrendering and Wilson shot him while surrendering.

However, if the bullet path is from the top of the head straight down through the body towards the ground, then Michael Brown would have been below Darren Wilson. This situation could **POSSIBLY** indicate that that Brown was either charging or kneeling.

Since both participants were about the same height, bullet paths that proceed through the top of the head downward are just not possible if both participants are standing. In this situation, Wilson would have to be holding the gun above the head of Brown and pointing straight down.

In the above characterizations, the word **POSSIBLY** is emphasized. Since the bullet paths have not been introduced as yet, the approximately equal heights of the participants is used as a guide to frame the investigation into the impact of equal heights on the potential explanations for the incident.

The weight differentials are significant here. Brown possessed an 80 pound weight difference over Darren Wilson. An 80 pound weight moving forward at a specific speed delivers tremendous momentum -- and force -- upon impact. So, if Brown were indeed shown to be charging, Wilson was clearly under threat of losing his life if Brown made impact.

Here is a simple experiment that will demonstrate the weight difference in a meaningful way. **Warning**: do this with your best friend. Open your hand, swing your hand at your friend, and strike the arm of your friend with the palm of your hand. Now, take a rock that weighs 5 pounds in your hand. Swing your hand holding the rock and strike the arm of your friend. Clearly, the hand with the rock delivers more momentum and more force, causing greater damage. Now, pick up an 40 pound rock and hold in both of your hands. Swing the rock at the arm of your best friend. A huge amount of momentum and force is delivered, causing perhaps death and certainly major damage.

On second thought: **DO NOT DO THIS EXPERIMENT WITH ANYONE**. You will probably kill your friend and be charged with murder. But, *if Michael Brown was charging*, this experiment is exactly the experiment performed by Michael Brown against Officer Wilson. Brown would have been delivering an equivalent impact based on a rock the size of 40 pounds at 40 miles per hour (to be proved later). This size rock moving at a charging speed would constitute a deadly weapon. So, Wilson would have been in immediate danger, potentially for loss of his life.

This issue will be discussed in more detail later.

At this point, be very careful to avoid forming any conclusions. Discussing implications of the heights and weights simply serves to identify potential avenues of investigation.

Map Of Fired Casings And Other Physical Evidence

After any shooting incident, law enforcement agencies dispatch a crime scene reconstruction team (NOT A SHOOTING INCIDENT RECONSTRUCTION TEAM). One of the objectives of this team is to create a map of the location of all of the physical evidence

The Grand Jury evidence contained the following map from the crime scene team in this case.

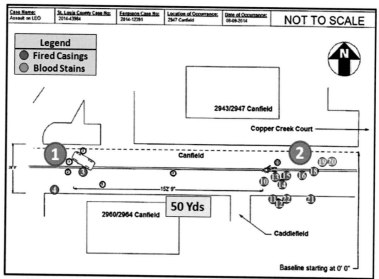

Figure 5: Map Of Locations Of Physical Evidence

The original map was all provided in black and white. For emphasis, color annotations were added by this author. The numbers in the red and green circles were provided by the crime scene team to locate specific items of evidence.

Several important categories of information are provided in this map.

A reference location is indicated on the map. This location will be the constant from which all future measurements are specified. As the map shows, the reference location is the intersection of Canfield Drive and Copper Creek Court.

Items 19 and 20, indicated in green, are the locations of fresh blood stains. Items indicated in red are the locations of fired casings. A few items in white circles represent other evidence items that are not of particular interest for the purposes of reconstruction. The final resting place of the body is also depicted on this map.

This map of locations of physical evidence provides some initial indications (or clues) as to the activity that occurred. Initial blood drops and the body are some distance apart. This distance indicates that Michael Brown moved between the time that he was first hit and the final resting place of the body.

Fired casings fall into two groups. The groups are indicated by blue markers. Blue marker one (1) represents the group of casings that are in the immediate area surrounding the abandoned vehicle of Officer Wilson. By definition in the Introduction, these casings are not of particular interest to this analysis. The location of these casings does serve to confirm that belief that a struggle occurred at the vehicle in which Brown attempted to wrest the firearm from Wilson and Wilson discharging his firearm in defense.

Blue marker two (2) identifies the group of casings of specific interest to this reconstruction. This group of casings are pretty much located between the first blood droppings and the location of the body on the ground. That fact indicates that these casings are the casings involved in the incident under analysis. Also, note that a total of twelve (12) casings were fired.

As stated a few paragraphs ago, the distance between the blood droppings shows that Brown was moving. The spread of the fired casings that same approximate distance **LIKELY** indicates that Wilson was also moving during the incident. In order to determine if Wilson was moving, characteristics of the ejection pattern of Wilson's pistol must be known. This whole issue will be addressed in a later chapter.

Another characteristic of the fired casing pattern is also apparent in the map. The casings spread not only down the street, as just discussed, but across the street. A double black line down the center of the street represents the middle of the street. Fired casings in group 2 spread from the center of the street, all the way across the street, to the edge of the sidewalk on the south side of the street.

The area covered by the casings in this group is found by the distance the casings spread down the street multiplied by the distance the casings spread across the street.

This area is quite large, probably much larger than the typical ejection pattern of a handgun. Covering such a large area further confirms that Wilson was probably moving when discharging his firearm.

An analysis of the fired casing area its relationship to the ejection pattern created by Officer Wilson's pistol will be discussed later.

Actual Locations of the Physical Evidence

Fortunately, the crime scene reconstruction team went further than simply drawing the locations of physical evidence on a map. A common reference point at the scene was chosen. From this reference point, the physical distance to each evidence item is carefully measured and recorded.

A table of locations that accompanies the map appears below.

ITEM NUMBER	Baseline (West from Copper Creek)	South of Baseline
St. Louis County Police Report 99-14-43984 Legend		
1. Black/Yellow Bracelet	208'2"	14'2"
2. Red Baseball cap	208'2"	16'3"
3. .40 cal Federal Spent Casing	201'1"	17'1"
4. .40 cal Federal Spent Casing	210'	29'2"
5. Black Bead Bracelet	201'3"	8'3"
6. White Nike Sandal (left foot)	179'7"	25'7"
7. White Nike Sandal (right foot)	136'	14'9"
8. Red Stain Driver Front Door Ext.		
9. Red Stain Driver Side Rear Door Ext.		
10. .40 cal Federal Spent Casing	56'	25'8"
11. .40 cal Federal Spent Casing	50'4"	33'9"
12. .40 cal Federal Spent Casing	50'1"	34'1"
13. .40 cal Federal Spent Casing	47'4"	24'
14. .40 cal Federal Spent Casing	43'	26'4"
15. .40 cal Federal Spent Casing	42'	23'11"
16. .40 cal Federal Spent Casing	36'10"	16'9"
17. Apparent Projectile	45'3"	10'10"
18. .40 cal Federal Spent Casing	33'4"	14'6"
19. Red Stain in Roadway	31'	11'9"
20. Red Stain in Roadway	26'7"	11'6"
21. .40 cal Federal Spent Casing	36'10"	31'10"
22. .40 cal Federal Spent Casing	47'4"	31'3"
Ferguson Marked Police Vehicle #108		
Driver Side Front Tire Center	206'3"	12'9"
Passenger Side Front Tire Center	203'8"	6'6"
Driver Side Rear Tire Center	197'3"	16'5"
Passenger Side Rear Tire Center	194'9"	10'4"
M. Brown's Location		
Left Foot	48'2"	15'6"
Right Foot	48'2"	13'6"
Left Hand	51'4"	15'3"
Right Hand	52'11"	12'3"
Head	53'6"	15'9"
Baseline runs East to West, on North Side of Canfield, with 0'0" starting at Copper Creek Ct.		

Last Casing

First Casing

Blood

Body

Reference Location

Table 2: Actual Locations Of Physical Evidence

This table contains a partial list of locations of primary interest to this reconstruction. The original table did not include the

36

rectangular identifiers. These rectangles were added by the author to indicate the locations of specific items of evidence. At the side of these rectangles, labels are provided that identify the specific items for reconstruction purposes.

For shooting incident reconstructions, this table is a treasure trove of very useful information.

At the bottom of the table, a solid red rectangle indicates the <u>Reference</u> location. From the description, the location is the intersection of Canfield Road and Copper Creek Court. This location was also identified on the map of locations of physical evidence.

Just above the solid red rectangle is a dashed red rectangle. This rectangle precisely locates the two hands of Brown's <u>Body</u> on the ground. By splitting the difference, the approximate center of Brown's body can be found.

Higher up in the table, the dashed green rectangle precisely locates the first drops of <u>Blood</u> shed by Brown. The first of these drops is where Brown likely turned towards Wilson. With casings so close to the location of the drops of blood, this location is the first location at which Brown was hit by one of Wilson's bullets.

The location of the <u>First Casing</u> found is highlighted by a solid blue rectangle. This casing serves as the starting boundary for the overall fired casing ejection area.

A second solid blue rectangle identifies the location of the <u>Last Casing</u> found by the crime scene team. Since this casing is near the body and the longest distance from the initial blood drops, this casing marks the ending boundary for the overall fired casing ejection area.

Each physical evidence item location is characterized by a distance to the west of the reference location and a distance south of the reference location. For instance, the last fired casing was found at 56' west of the reference location and 25' 8" south of the reference location.

These precise locations will be used to place markers onto a Google Maps photo. With some simple addition and subtraction, distances between various evidence items can also be computed.

Distances are an important element of reconstruction. A distance enables determination as to whether the bullet trajectories were straight and flat or curved. These same distances can also reveal whether a participant was moving or standing still. When employed with wound paths inside the body, distances can also help to determine the body orientation of the shooter, the victim, and even the orientation and angle of the firearm in the hand of the shooter.

Firearms and Ammunition Involved

As the evidence location shows, fired casings were found across a wide area. In order to interpret this dispersion of fired casings, both the types of firearms and types of ammunition used are important to know.

In this case, only Officer Wilson discharged a firearm. Therefore, information about his firearm and his ammunition is important.

According to the Crime Lab Weapon Analysis Report in the Grand Jury evidence, Officer Wilson used the firearm and ammunition shown below:

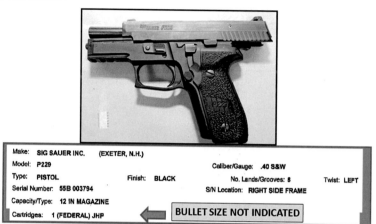

Make: **SIG SAUER INC.** (EXETER, N.H.)				
Model: **P229**		Caliber/Gauge: **.40 S&W**		
Type: **PISTOL**	Finish: **BLACK**	No. Lands/Grooves: **8**	Twist: **LEFT**	
Serial Number: **55B 003794**		S/N Location: **RIGHT SIDE FRAME**		
Capacity/Type: **12 IN MAGAZINE**				
Cartridges: **1 (FEDERAL) JHP**		BULLET SIZE NOT INDICATED		

Figure 6: Firearm and Ammunition Used

On the day of the incident, Officer Wilson carried a Sig Sauer model P229 in caliber 40 Smith & Wesson. This pistol is likely Wilson's regular duty weapon. From this image and others that were available, the pistol appears to be in stock configuration. Some internal enhancements may have been made, such as a trigger job to reduce trigger pull, but no information exists in the reports to indicate that any modifications were performed

This same Crime Lab Weapon Analysis Report also indicates that the magazine that accompanied the pistol was loaded with 12 cartridges. Although not mentioned, these cartridges were likely unfired. Since the evidence location map shows 12 fired casings, Officer Wilson probably performed a tactical reload of his empty magazine with this full magazine.

As far as the ammunition is concerned, a lack of important detail is apparent. This report does not indicate anything more than the name of the manufacturer, Federal. In order to obtain an ejection pattern for this incident, more detailed information is necessary.

However, the Firearms Report does include some additional information that helps to identify the ammunition that was used.

```
QB1 - COPPER JHP BULLET (DAMAGED), .40 CAL., 6-L, FROM "FPD VEH. 108". (158.0 gr.) {CSU #7}
QB2 - COPPER JHP BULLET (DAMAGED), .40 CAL., 6-L, FROM BROWN'S "RIGHT SIDE OF BACK". (177.0 gr.) {CSU #14}
QB3 - COPPER JHP BULLET (DAMAGED), .40 CAL., 6-L, FROM BROWN'S "RIGHT SIDE OF CHEST". (152.6 gr.) {CSU #15}
QB4 - COPPER JHP BULLET (DAMAGED), .40 CAL., 6-L, FROM BROWN'S "RIGHT SIDE OF HEAD". (151.0 gr.) {CSU #16}
QB5 - COPPER JHP BULLET (DAMAGED), .40 CAL., 6-L, FROM "ROADWAY". (180.2 gr.) {CSU #17}
```

Figure 7: List of Fired Bullets Found At The Scene

Five (5) discharged bullets were found at the scene in various locations, such as inside the body of Brown. All of these bullets were caliber 40 Smith & Wesson. Therefore, these bullets were likely discharged by Officer Wilson during the incident. All of these bullets were jacketed, hollow point (JHP) bullets.

Most interesting is that the bullets ranged in various sizes: 158 grain to 180 grain. Wilson was using lots of different sizes of ammunition in his pistol on that day. From the listing that identifies the items of evidence, all of the casings found were Federal 40 Smith & Wesson.

All of the fired casings were Federal 40 Smith and Wesson. All of the found, discharged bullets were 40 Smith & Wesson, JHP. All of the unfired cartridges in Wilson's pistol were Federal 40 Smith & Wesson JHP.

A very safe conclusion is that Officer Wilson used Federal 40 Smith & Wesson JHP cartridges with bullet weights from 158 grain to 180 grain.

Unfortunately, Federal manufactures a lot of different brands that meet these characteristics. This issue will be discussed later.

Wounds and Wound Paths

Included in the Grand Jury evidence was a copy of the Autopsy Report prepared by the St. Louis County Office of The Medical Examiner. This report describes 11 wounds.

For purposes of this analysis, only the first five (5) wounds are of interest. A summary of these wounds appears in the table below.

Number	Entrance	Direction	Exit
1	**Vertex of the scalp** 7.87" above right auditory meatus Midline of vertex of head	Downward, rightward	**At rest** within soft tissue of right lateral face
2, 3	**Central forehead** 2.76" above right auditory meatus 0.79" right of anterior midline of head	Downward, slightly backward and rightward	**Right jaw** 2.17" below right auditory meatus 4.33" right of anterior midline of head
4	**Upper right chest** 6.30" below right auditory meatus 3.54" right of anterior midline of chest	Slightly downward, Slightly backward	**At rest** Within soft tissue of right chest (posterier 3rd right intercostal space)
5	**Lateral right chest** 7.87" below right auditory meatus 8.66" right of anterior midline of chest	Downward, backward	**At rest** Within soft tissue of lateral right back (fractures 8th rib)

Table 3: Summary Of Most Destructive Wounds

These specific wounds were chosen for evaluation because these are the wounds that were the most destructive. This selection of wounds will become apparent shortly.

Rather than repeat the pages and pages of detailed descriptions, this table summarizes the most important aspects of each of the selected wounds. Wound numbers in the left most column are the same identification numbers that were used in the Medical Examiner's Report. Each wound is characterized by an entrance

41

location on the body, a direction of travel in the body, and a final resting place.

Each entrance location is clearly described. Reference locations are the right auditory meatus and the anterior midline of the head. Specific locations are an offset from these reference locations. This specification will be clearly explained at a later time.

In the original report, entrance locations were defined in metric units -- centimeters of offset from the reference location. Appendix A contains the same table as above, with the offsets in centimeters.

These wounds are also divided into bullet paths in this table. Wound 1 is a single bullet path. Wounds 2 and 3 comprise a second bullet path in which the bullet entered Brown's body, exited, then re-entered the body, finally coming to a resting position, still in the body.

The first bullet path of interest starts with the entrance identified as wound 1. This bullet entered the vertex of the scalp and penetrated the right parietal lobe of the brain and the right temporal lobe of the brain. In simple terms, the bullet crashed through several lobes of the brain. Even a person without a medical degree can see that this bullet and bullet path were probably the cause of the death of Brown. Certainly, ***brain damage*** justifies selection of this wound and wound path as the most destructive of the wound paths.

As the second bullet path of interest, wounds 2, 3, and 4 combine into a single bullet path. The bullet entered into the central forehead of the body. This bullet traveled downward, through the right eye, the inferior right orbital bone, and the soft tissue of the face, exiting the right jaw. This bullet then re-entered the right chest, continued downward, and came to rest near the lungs. Clearly, this bullet caused a lot of damage, destroying the right eye and a bunch of bone structure. But, this bullet causing mostly **_bone damage_** was not as damaging as the bullet that crushed major parts of the brain, thus justifying these wounds as the next most destructive of the wound paths.

Another important wound path is associated with wound 5. This bullet path entered the lateral right chest, coming to a rest in the soft tissue of the lateral right back. This bullet path resulted in disruptive tissue damage. **_Tissue disruption_** is not as damaging as the crushing of bones, qualifying this bullet and bullet path as the third most destructive of the wound paths.

All of these bullet paths moved in a downward direction. This downward direction is from the top of the body, through the body, towards the feet. While some bullet paths were slightly angled towards the rear, the bullet paths of each of these entrances is practically parallel to the vertical axis of the body, when the body is standing straight up.

All of these bullets ultimately remained in the body. This result is not surprising given the body structure and weight of Brown. Crushing through brain, bone, and heavy tissue creates far more drag on a bullet than the drag on a bullet through the air. Brown was structurally big and very heavy at 289 pounds. That large mass of brain, bone, and tissue exerted significant drag, significantly slowing the bullet forward velocity.

No soot or stippling was found on any entrance wound.

The discussion describing each wound clearly states that the wound did not exhibit any soot or stippling. Soot is a layer of burnt powder. Stippling is un-burnt powder that causes punctate abrasions resulting in petechia. In layman terms, the un-burnt powder is a crystaline structure that punches a small hole in the skin, causing bleeding into the surrounding skin. In even simpler terms, the skin exhibits small, bloody spots.

A complete absence of soot or stippling provides a clue as to the distance between the shooter and the target. As the shooter moves further and further from the target, the soot and stippling spread out over a wider and wider area. At some distance, the target does not exhibit any soot or stippling.

A lot of variables affect the distance at which soot and stippling disappears, such as the length of the barrel, the type of firearm, the type of ammunition and the angle of the target surface to the bullet trajectory. In order to more accurately characterize the distance at which soot and stippling disappears, a soot and stippling distance test must be accomplished. This test will be discussed later.

None of the key wound paths are characterized by entries in the back or rear of Brown's body.

All of the wound path entries were in the top of the head. A single wound path entry was in the upper body, but this was a continuation of a wound path initiated in the top of the head.

Summarizing the other wound paths reveals the lack of importance of these wounds for purposes of this reconstruction. Wounds 6 and

7 form a bullet path through the upper right arm. A bullet path through the right forearm is created by wounds 8 and 9. Two graze wounds are created by bullets. Wound 10 is a graze wound through the right bicep. A graze wound through the near right thumb is identified as wound 11. These wounds simply did not cause the extent of damage as the wounds in the first category which are the basis for the reconstruction.

Typically, a medical examiner or coroner's report contains a diagram that shows the entrance and exit wounds and the bullet paths through the body. The report released with the Grand Jury evidence did not contain such a diagram. So, this author created the diagram.

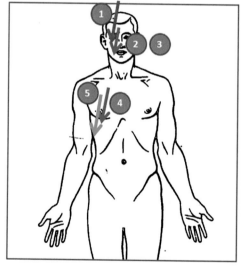

Figure 8: Bullet Paths Based On Medical Examiner Report

Wound 1 initiates the bullet path through the top of the head. This bullet path is shown as a red arrow. Wounds 2, 3, and 4 create the bullet path through the forehead, just below the scalp. Blue arrows depict the this bullet path caused by the entry, exit, and re-entry of a single bullet. Wound 5 is a separate bullet path resulting from the entry into the right side of the upper chest. This path appears as a green arrow in the figure.

All of the paths are directed rightward, according to the autopsy report. Rightward means towards the right side of Brown's body, hence forming a left to right path relative to the body.

This visual depiction clearly illustrations the downward and rightward path of the bullets. These vertical paths for all of the bullets immediately bring into question any claims that Brown was surrendering.

If Brown were walking towards Wilson surrendering, Wilson's pistol would have to be above the head of Brown and pointed downward and angled back towards Wilson. On the surface, this hand position does not make much sense. This specific issue will be investigated later.

Police Investigation Report Summary

Included in the Grand Jury evidence was an investigation report prepared and submitted by the St. Louis County Police Department. This report is identified by report number **14-43984.**

For purposes of this reconstruction, the report contained a number of important elements. A summary of the sequence of events immediately prior to and during the shooting incident was provided. Additionally, the position of the body was carefully and fairly accurately described.

The first part of the sequence of events appears as follows:

After arriving at the complex, Sergeant [omitted] briefly spoke with Police Officer Darren Wilson, DSN 609, of the Ferguson Police Department. Sergeant [omitted] provided the following information about his conversation with P.O. Darren Wilson. P.O. Darren Wilson indicated to him that he had been involved in a shooting and the subject of the shooting was now deceased. Sergeant [omitted] indicated P.O. Darren Wilson had previously told the subject, who had been walking down the middle of Canfield Drive with another male, to get out of the roadway and over to the sidewalk. Sergeant [omitted] indicated P.O. Darren Wilson attempted to exit his vehicle and contact the males. As he attempted to exit his vehicle, a struggle involving the driver's side door began after the subject shut the driver's side door on him. The subject would not let P.O. Darren Wilson get out of his vehicle. The subject began assaulting P.O. Darren Wilson through the driver's side window while P.O. Darren Wilson was still inside his police vehicle. The assault escalated to the point where the subject tried to take P.O. Darren Wilson's firearm and P.O. Darren Wilson fired at least one gunshot while inside the vehicle.

> **P.O. Darren Wilson indicated to him that he had been involved in a shooting and the subject of the shooting was now deceased. Sergeant [omitted] indicated P.O. Darren Wilson had previously told the subject, who had been walking down the middle of Canfield Drive with another male, to get out of the roadway and over to the sidewalk. Sergeant [omitted] indicated P.O. Darren Wilson attempted to exit his vehicle and contact the males. As he attempted to exit his vehicle, a struggle involving the driver's side door began after the subject shut the driver's side door on him. The subject would not let P.O. Darren Wilson get out of his vehicle. The subject began assaulting P.O. Darren Wilson through the driver's side window while P.O. Darren Wilson was still inside his police vehicle. The assault escalated to the point where the subject tried to take P.O. Darren Wilson's firearm and P.O. Darren Wilson fired at least one gunshot while inside the vehicle.**

St Louis County Police Department, Report 14-43984, P. 3

This snippet explains the actions of Brown and Wilson at the vehicle of Officer Wilson prior to the shooting portion of the incident. According to this summary, the following activities occurred at the vehicle:

- Wilson ordered Brown and friend to get off roadway
- Wilson was trapped in his vehicle by Brown
- Brown tried to take Wilson's firearm
- Wilson fired at least one gunshot.

The narrative does not explain whether Wilson intentionally discharged his firearm. However, extensive forensic literature exists that clearly demonstrates that an unintended discharge can occur during a struggle over a firearm. Either way, proof exists that the firearm certainly discharged.

According to the earlier Physical Evidence Location Map, two (2) fired casings were found near Wilson's vehicle. Items 3 and 4 were fired casing in caliber 40 Smith & Wesson, which was the cartridge used by Wilson in his firearm.

After this initial confrontation, the report continues describing the sequence of events:

> The subject ran away from the vehicle and ran east on Canfield Drive. P.O. Darren Wilson exited his vehicle and gave chase on foot. During the foot chase, the subject turned around and began running toward P.O. Darren Wilson. P.O. Darren Wilson indicated to Sergeant that, as the subject was charging toward him, P.O. Darren Wilson fired his weapon to stop the subject from assaulting him further.

The subject ran away from the vehicle and ran east on Canfield Drive. P.O. Darren Wilson exited his vehicle and gave chase on foot. During the foot chase, the subject turned around and began running toward P.O. Darren Wilson. P.O. Darren Wilson indicated to Sergeant [omitted] that, as the subject was charging toward him, P.O. Darren Wilson fired his weapon to stop the subject from assaulting him further.

St Louis County Police Department, Report 14-43984, P. 3

This section of the report explains the actions of Wilson and Brown during the actual shooting portion of the incident.

According to this summary, the following actions occurred during the shooting portion of the incident:

- Wilson gave chase on foot

48

- Brown turned and ran towards Wilson
- Brown was charging Wilson
- Wilson shot Brown to stop Brown from assaulting

This short description concisely enumerates the law enforcement theory of the shooting incident. **The essential elements here are that Brown turned, Brown charged, Wilson shot.**

At this point, blind acceptance of this statement of events is a great error and should be avoided. This statement is one theory of the incident. This theory of the evidence may not even stand up to close inspection of the physical and other evidence. Most importantly, this depiction of the actions should be used to identify multiple possible and reasonable alternative explanations.

A close reading of this description clearly identifies the core element -- Brown was charging. Form this core element, other possible and reasonable explanations can be identified.

At this point, several common sense alternative descriptions of Brown's actions come to mind for consideration:

- Brown was bent forward charging
- Brown was standing and surrendering
- Brown was standing and surrendering with his head bowed
- Brown was kneeling and surrendering
- Brown was flat on the ground

This range of alternative theories of Brown's possible positions is fairly extensive, covering everything from totally upright to flat.

Clearly, ridiculous options need not be considered. Brown was not standing on his head or doing cartwheels.

All of these options assume that Brown was facing towards Wilson. If Brown had his back towards Wilson, entry wounds would have been in the back. Back entry wounds would have been clearly identified by the Medical Examiner and highlighted by Dr. Michael Baden, the independent Medical Examiner.

Another important aspect of the Investigation Report is the very clear description of the position of the body.

> Detective _____ observed Brown was lying on his stomach with his head facing approximately west and his feet facing approximately east on Canfield Drive. Brown was wearing a light gray T-shirt, blue underwear, khaki shorts, a black belt, and tall yellow socks with apparent black marijuana leaves on them.
>
> The right side of Brown's face was resting on the roadway. Apparent blood was on the roadway near Brown's head and had traveled in a western direction away from Brown. Brown's left arm was partially bent at the elbow with his left hand near the waist of his pants with his palm up. There was nothing in his left hand. Brown's right arm was straight and slightly away from the lower portion of his body, in an approximately northeast direction. His right palm was face up. There was nothing in his right hand.

> **Detective [omitted] observed Brown was lying on his stomach with his head facing approximately west and his feet facing approximately east on Canfield Drive. [Clothing description ...]**
>
> **The right side of Brown's face was resting on the roadway. Apparent blood was on the roadway near Brown's head and had travelled in a western direction away from Brown. Brown's left arm was partially bent at the elbow with his left hand near the waist of his pants with his palm up. There was nothing in his left hand. Brown's right arm was straight and slightly away from the lower portion of his body, in an approximately northeast direction. His right palm was face up. There was nothing in his right hand.**

St Louis County Police Department, Report 14-43984, P. 7

Again, a summary of the key elements of this description is in order:

- Brown was face down on his stomach
- Brown had his arms down by his side
- Brown had both palms face up

A few pages ago, four possible theories of Brown's behavior immediately before his death were presented. An important evaluation is to determine which of these possible behaviors by Brown could have resulted in a body in this position.

Witness Statement Summary

About 23 witnesses provided testimony regarding the behavior of Michael Brown at the time of the shooting. A summary of the witness statements, except for Dorian Johnson, appears in the table below:

Category	Number Statements	Comment
Charging	4	Includes Wilson
Walking Back	4	Casual Demeanor
Turned Around	5	Shot As Turning
Falling	2	On His Knees (1)
Surrender	7	Hands Up (6)

Table 4: Summary Of Witness Statements

Dorian Johnson's statement is not included in this tabulation. Johnson was walking down the street with Brown and is the percipient witness in this case. His statements are considered independently.

A more complete summary with locations of the witnesses, short extracts of their statements, and the locations of those statements in the Grand Jury evidence appears in Appendix B.

This table reveals quite a bit about the witness statements. **The range of statements about the position of Brown prior to his being shot covers pretty much the same range of possible theories of his behavior that were outlined above as alternate theories.** The witnesses cover every position from perfectly vertical to almost horizontal. Several potential body positions were not indicated by any of the witnesses. Positions *NOT* indicated include Brown lying on the ground, Brown sitting, or Brown walking forward with his head in a submissive position. Moreover, none of the witnesses claimed that Brown had his back to Wilson when Wilson shot Brown, despite the claims of some news organizations.

Such a wide range of statements suggests that eye witness testimony generally lacks credibility. Unfortunately, this conclusion is often true. However, **witness testimony can serve to corroborate the physical and scientific evidence. Witness testimony can also be refuted by physical and scientific evidence**.

Percipient Witness Statement Summary

At the time of the incident, Dorian Johnson was walking eastward on Canfield Drive with Michael Brown. Johnson was the closest to Brown at the time of the shooting. Being at the location makes Johnson the percipient witness. Therefore, his statements about the incident require special emphasis and consideration. Special consideration and emphasis means that the statements should be given careful scrutiny, but not necessarily accepted as absolute fact.

52

Johnson's statements fall into two categories. Some of Johnson's declarations identify the **locations** of the Brown and Wilson. Other statements describe the **interactions** between Brown and Wilson.

A list of the key declarations about **locations** made my Johnson include the following:

"I stood and watched face-to-face as every shot was fired"
                    -- Volume 4, P 124, L 21-22

"he gets probably to the curve of the driveway"
                    -- Volume 4, P 120, L 14-15

"the officer ... he's passing the third vehicle"
                    -- Volume 4, P 120, L16-17

These statements are identified according to the locations in the Grand Jury evidence testimony documents. The released evidence did not include a specific map to accompany these locations. In these statements, the pronoun "he" refers to Michael Brown.

Statements made by Johnson regarding the interactions between Brown and Wilson are as follows:

"He just kind of stopped and turned around at the officer"
                    -- Volume 4, P 120, L 9-10

"I see Big Mike turn around and face the officer"
                    -- Volume 4, P 121, L 3-4

"he's face-to-face with the officer, but not so close"
                    -- Volume 4, P 120, L 11-12

"he never started running"
                              -- Volume 4, P 123, L 7

"His body kind of just went down and fell"
                              -- Volume 4, P 124, L 21-22

"Q: he never like got on his knees ...?"
"A: He was falling"
                              -- Volume 4, P 125, L 17-19

The statements above are not in the order of testimony. Rather, all of these statements are placed in the order necessary to provide a cohesive understanding of the locations and the interactions.

Statements made by non-expert witnesses during testimony are often a bit jumbled. This jumbling results from a number of factors. In this case, the witness is not an expert, but a layman. By definition, statements by a layman are not going to be precisely and clearly formulated as statements made by an expert. Another important factor is that the statements are answers to questions formulated by an attorney. So, the sequence of answers is guided by the attorney asking the questions.

However, the goal here is to understand exactly the information being provided by the witness. In this way, the statement can be used as corroboration or can be refuted by physical or scientific evidence, depending on the theory of the case.

Johnson clearly identifies himself as the percipient witness. Wilson is passing the "third vehicle" on Canfield Drive. Brown gets to the curve of the driveway, probably the corner of Canfield Drive and Copper Creek Court. Copper Creek Court probably makes the most sense here, because this location is closest to where the first drops of blood were found, according to the map of physical evidence.

Sorting through the statements by Johnson regarding the interactions, a fairly clear picture of the interaction between Wilson and Brown appears:

- Brown turned to face Wilson

- Brown is face to face with Wilson

- Wilson shot Brown

- Brown drops down to the ground

In simple terms, Johnson claims that Brown turned, implying that Brown was going to surrender, and that Wilson executed Brown. Johnson also clearly states that Brown never went to his knees.

Clearly, this statement contradicts the theory of the incident that was promulgated by the Investigation Report. Moreover, this alleged sequence of events confirms the possibility of one of the alternate theories that was proposed earlier based on key elements of the theory proposed in the Investigation Report.

As with the Investigation Report, this statement of the sequence of events represents a possible theory and should not be taken as absolute fact. Both this theory and the theory proposed in the Investigation Report must be systematically and scientifically evaluated.

Summary Of The Grand Jury Evidence

A number of important elements of the Grand Jury evidence form the foundation of the systematic and scientific analysis. These elements are summarize below:

- Wilson and Brown were about the same height.
- Wilson was 210 pounds; Brown was 289 pounds.

- Locations of the first and last casing were carefully measured.
- Locations of the first blood stains and the body were carefully measured.

- Darren Wilson carried a Sig Sauer P-229 pistol chambered in caliber 40 Smith & Wesson
- Darren Wilson utilized Federal cartridges with bullet weights ranging from 158 grains to 180 grains in weight

- The key wound paths started in the top of the head
- The key wound paths proceeded downward through the body
- No soot or stippling was found at the entrance of any of the wounds
- None of the bullet paths are associated with an entrance wound in the back or rear of Brown

- The Investigation Report alleges that Brown was charging
- Multiple theories of the incident can be identified from the Investigation Report

- Dorian Johnson, the percipient witness, claims that Brown was shot just after turning to face Wilson

- Other witness statements cover a wide range of possible theories

Comparison With Other Evidence Summaries

The evidence supplied to the Grand Jury by the St. Louis County Police is very typical of the type of evidence supplied in shooting incidents.

Other cases often involve additional bullet impacts, over and above those created in the body of the victim. In those cases, data is usually provided that summarizes the impacts. Rods or dowels are used to determine impact height, upward and downward angles, and left to right angles. Individuals collecting this data differ in the level of precision. One criminalist may simply state downward angled while another criminalist might record a 20^0 downward angle.

The evidence provided in this case does compare well with evidence provided in other cases. However, the evidence provided does possess one major flaw, as does the evidence provided in these cases.

As with almost every case, in the thousands of pages of evidence provided, the evidence is just summarized. From the list of raw evidence, a theory of the incident is proposed. _**However, the manner in which the raw evidence leads to the theory of the incident is never provided**_.

This statement is clearly true for the evidence in this case. As the summary of the evidence and the detailed evaluation both reveal, multiple alternate theories of the incident are available to the trier of fact (the jury) based on the evidence.

The good news is that the evidence collected forms an excellent foundation to evaluate the alternate theories. However, some additional data must be collected, some science must be employed, and a few systematic principles, procedures, and techniques must be utilized.

Systematic Shooting Reconstruction Features

The primary objective of shooting incident reconstruction is to evaluate alternate theories of a shooting incident. An immediate result of a reconstruction is to determine which theory of the incident best describes the who, what, when, where, and how of the incident.

Systematic and scientific shooting incident reconstruction cannot explain why a shooting incident was perpetrated. Nor can a reconstruction attempt to exploit intent. Both of these aspects of a shooting incident are in the head of the perpetrator. Unless you can read minds, these aspects of a shooting incident are off limits for purposes of shooting reconstruction.

A systematic approach to shooting incident reconstruction exhibits a number of features. Each of these features is discussed below.

Declaration Of Basic Features

**A systematic approach to shooting incident reconstruction is clearly based on scientific principles.**

Science can be either deductive or inductive in nature. Both types of science are specifically utilized in a systematic approach.

Deductive science starts with general principles and makes specific predictions. Bullet trajectories are based on a general set of equations of motion evolved from work of Sir Isaac Newton. By using the appropriate parameters, such as drag and ballistic coefficients, specific predictions are made regarding the bullet path of a particular caliber of ammunition. General equations predict specific bullet path.

In contrast, inductive science uses specific data and makes generalizations. Ejection pattern tests involve discharge of a semi-automatic pistol to place ejected casings on the ground. A summary of the pattern is created to identify the pattern for the class of pistol used when combined with the class of ammunition employed. Specific casing locations predict general ejection patterns.

A systematic approach to shooting incident reconstruction utilizes actual evidence data, the scientific basis, additional data collection, along with witness testimony in a logically consistent, cohesive manner.

All of these elements must contribute to an explanation of the shooting incident that clearly answers the specific questions -- who, what, when, where, and how.

Furthermore, none of these elements can contradict the explanation, unless scientifically refuted, as described below.

At the heart of the shooting incident reconstruction in this case is the integration of the physical trajectory (deductive science) of the 40 Smith & Wesson caliber bullet with the ejection pattern (inductive science) of the Sig P-229 pistol, as carried by Wilson. A second step involves combining this integrated trajectory/ejection pattern with the physical locations of the fired casings from the Investigation Report. Laws of momentum and force are then used to evaluate the actual threat faced by Wilson when charged by Brown.

Trajectory, ejection pattern, physical location of fired casings, and physics of momentum and force all work together logically to explain what really happened at the time of the shooting.

A systematic approach to shooting incident reconstruction evaluates multiple theories of the incident that make reasonable sense.

Presupposing a theory of the incident is a form of bias. Obviously, this form of bias colors your thinking. Identification and evaluation of multiple theories of an incident demonstrates objectivity.

However, some theories simply do not make common sense. In this case, multiple theories have been identified that make common sense -- standing and surrendering, charging, kneeling, flat on the ground.

The definition of reasonable depends a lot upon the context and the other evidence provided. In this case, none of the bullet paths are characterized by an entry wound in the back. Therefore, this alternate theory does not make sense in this situation.

Similarly, other alternative theories can be formulated that do not make much sense. For instance, considering a theory of the incident in which Brown is standing on his head would be a waste of time. No witness made any statement that would lead to this theory. Given the circumstances around the incident, Brown simply would not have been performing any action such as this action.

A systematic approach combines physical evidence, experimental data, and mathematics, science, and physics to evaluate various aspects of a shooting incident

Individual items of evidence cannot explain a shooting incident. Wound paths by themselves are not meaningful without knowing the bullet trajectory path through the air. The spread of fired casing locations can only be evaluated if the ejection pattern of the firearm with similar ammunition is known.

Wound paths are typically available as evidence. The relationship between wound paths and bullet trajectory paths requires knowledge of some underlying physics of trajectories along with **visualization techniques that combine wound paths and bullet trajectory path physics.** Using these visualization techniques, alternate theories of the incident can be evaluated for scientific reasonableness.

The spread of fired casing locations is also generally available as evidence. An ejection pattern describes the landing zone of fired casings when a firearm is discharged with specific ammunition. This pattern can only be determined by performing a test fire and identifying the landing zone of the fired casings. **Using mathematical convolution (combining) techniques, the relationship between fired casing locations and the ejection pattern is determined.** This relationship enables evaluation of the shooting locations, indicating whether the shooter was moving, the direction of movement, or standing still.

In each of the examples above, combining the physical evidence, physics, and collected data provides additional insight into the incident. This insight (scientific reasonableness, shooter movement) was simply not available by just considering the physical evidence alone. Thus, using combinations is perhaps the most important feature of the systematic approach.

A systematic approach to shooting incident reconstruction is based upon principles, procedures, and techniques.

The approach outlined in this book is based upon some very specific principles, procedures, and techniques.

A principle is defined as a fundamental truth or proposition that serves as the foundation for a system of belief or behavior or for a chain of reasoning. Some of the fundamental truths employed in this systematic approach to shooting reconstruction include the following:

- trajectories (bullet paths) are straight and flat for the first 25 yards, regardless of caliber

- ejection patterns are characterized by direction, distance, and width, regardless of type of ammunition

- trajectories and ejection patterns form a coordinate system with the shooter at the intersection

- amount of soot and stippling decreases as the shooter moves away from the target

- if an object is standing still and a moving object impacts, the moving object imparts a force to the standing object

- momentum can be used to compare the ability of two objects to stay on a straight line path prior to impact.

- force can be used to compare the effect of various impacting objects on an impacted object.

- two cartridges with the same momentum possess equivalent capability to sustain a straight and flat bullet path.

- a force imparted to an standing object by a moving object can cause damage or destruction

- bullet paths in the body are characterized by geometric specifications -- reference points, lines, and angles

- dowels can be used to replication the bullet path in a body based on the geometric specifications

- the bullet path through the body provides information about the position of the body at the time of impact

- the bullet path through the body can also help to locate the relative positions of the shooter and the victim

- overlay of ejection patterns with the locations of fired casings can give insight into movement of the shooter and the victim

- the resting position of a body can provide insight into the actions of the body prior to its resting place

All of these principles are derived from specific laws of science. The scientific basis for these principles will be described later.

A procedure is a set of steps or actions that are performed in a specific order. The procedure used in **THIS** reconstruction is as follows:

- gather the relevant physical evidence, as previously outlined

- identify multiple theories of the incident

- identify and gather additional data as needed

- evaluate the multiple theories of the incident using the physical evidence, the additional data, visualizations, and science

- identify the specific theory of the incident justified by the physical evidence, the additional data, visualizations, and science

- rebut the other theories of the incident justified by the physical evidence, the additional data, visualization, and science

- use witness statements to confirm the specific theory of the incident using the physical evidence, the additional data, visualizations, and science

- rebut witness statements using the physical evidence, the additional data, visualizations, and science

- corroborate the selected theory of the incident by an analysis of the physics of impact and the final body position

For the most part, these procedural steps can be followed in a large percentage of shooting reconstructions. However, since the issues that are faced in a specific shooting incident are wide ranging, some of these steps may have to be deleted, other steps may be added.

A technique is a skillful or efficient way of doing or achieving something. Some very skillful techniques are employed in this reconstruction.

- dowels are used to accurately reconstruct the path of a bullet through the body

- an ejection pattern study provides specific characterization of the ejection pattern of a class of firearm with class of ammunition

- a firearm discharge study determines the distance at which soot and stippling no longer appear at an entrance wound.

- visualization with actors clearly corroborates or refutes a specific theory of a shooting incident

- the laws of physics predict a lot of the consequences of actions by various participants in the shooting incident.

The techniques employed here are easily performed by an person conducting a reconstruction investigation. A simple device is constructed to replicate bullet paths. Even the physics formulas are either implemented in easily obtained computer programs or are fairly simple to compute.

A systematic approach to shooting incident reconstruction is repeatable by others.

Every aspect of reconstruction outlined so far is easily performed by a person who is reasonably competent and knowledgeable in this area.

Repeatability is one hallmark of the scientific method. If approaches are used that cannot be independently replicated, then the approach is of questionable value.

A systematic approach to shooting incident reconstruction is the product of clear and objective logic, not subjective or personal experience.

Underlying every aspect of this systematic approach is that conclusions must be justified based on physical evidence, science, collected data, and clear logic that uses this information.

In a systematic approach, justification based on personal experience of the analysis simply has no place. When an analyst in any area of forensics claims that a conclusion is justified based on "experience", this analyst is being unscientific. This indicates that a person with more or less experience will potentially arrive at a different conclusion. That result is specifically the nature of subjective evaluation.

A systematic approach to shooting incident reconstruction employs visualization with charts, graphs, drawings, photos, and videos to clarify specific aspects of the incident.

Most people have heard the adage, "A picture is worth a thousand words." This adage is definitely applicable to shooting reconstructions.

A visual representation clarifies relationships of objects and orientations of objects, eliminating dispute. As in this case, visualization with actors clearly demonstrates the relationship between a specific theory of the incident, the positions of the shooter and the victim, and the bullet paths. Once these relationships are visualized, a specific theory of the incident emerges as the clear explanation.

A systematic approach to shooting incident reconstruction utilizes specific eyewitness testimony, if available, to support the explanation and rebuts witness testimony that makes no sense, both based on some combination of science, actual evidence, additional collected data and visualization.

Eyewitness testimony can cover a wide range of possibilities, can be contradictory, and very frustrating. This case precisely demonstrates these specific issues.

However, despite these issues, eyewitness testimony cannot be ignored. Such testimony needs to be carefully considered and evaluated.

Any evaluation of eyewitness testimony must be based upon some combination of science, actual evidence, additional collected data and visualization.

Support of eyewitness testimony for a specific theory of the incident must be justified based on some combination of the elements above. Eyewitness testimony cannot be deemed valid just because that testimony supports a particular theory.

Similarly, rebuttal of eyewitness testimony that contradicts a specific theory must also be justified on some combination of the above elements.

In this case, Dorian Johnson claims that Brown turned and was shot. This statement is rebutted in the analysis by showing that the bullet path through the body would have been quite different from the actual bullet paths. Science of bullet trajectories along with visualization are employed to exactly demonstrate the different in bullet paths.

Johnson's testimony is not rejected simply because his theory contradicts the statements by other witnesses that claim that Brown was charging. Science and visualization are used to show that Johnson's claims about the incident are simply not possible.

A systematic approach to shooting incident reconstruction often employs anecdotal evidence or exemplary evidence or analogy of similar interactions in other situations.

Comparison is a valid logical technique to demonstrate that claims or scientific analysis coincide with similar, practical situations.

Several examples of this appear in this case reconstruction. Using the physics of momentum and force, predictions are made that show that Brown charging can cause heavily body damage on impact. An anecdotal example is used to demonstrate that this prediction coincides with common experiences. This example is that of a famous impact by one football player against another football player that resulted in broken ribs.

A systematic approach to shooting incident reconstruction is based on precise accuracy, if possible, or reasonableness, if not possible.

Analysts, physicists, mathematicians all would prefer to deal with complete accuracy. Many times that is possible. Sometimes, however, reasonable approximations must be used.

Often resources are a problem when performing a shooting reconstruction. An incident occurs inside a 1963 Toyota Camry. Finding such a vehicle can be a problem. However, the issue turns out to be the dimensions of the cabin of the vehicle. Any vehicle with similar cabin dimensions, within a few inches, will suffice to make valid conclusions.

In this case, the exact ammunition used by Darren Wilson was poorly specified in the Firearms Report. The manufacturer of the ammunition was identified. The brand was not identified. However, a number of fired bullets were found that ranged in weight between 158 grains and 180 grains. Ejection pattern testing was performed with ammunition by the same manufacturer that ranged between 165 grains and 180 grains. The reasonableness of this selection is justified by performing a physics analysis of the momentum of this range of ammunition.

Using a reasonable set of options does not invalidate the evidence, simply because the selection of ammunition was not exact. Identification of the exact ammunition simply was not provided.

Reflection Of Uncertainty

Every analysis performed by humans possesses some amount of uncertainty. Effects of uncertainty must be reflected in a systematic and scientific based shooting reconstruction.

Uncertainty appears at multiple levels in a shooting reconstruction.

The most important level concerns a specific theory of the incident. Early identification of alternate theories of the incident is the manner in which a reconstruction accommodates uncertainty.

Another level of uncertainty occurs when evaluating the impact of conditions controlled by specific dimensions, such as the cabin dimensions in a vehicle. This kind of uncertainty can be handled in a number of ways.

One additional approach has already been identified -- use reasonably similar dimensions. A vehicle with cabin dimensions within a few inches serves as a reasonable substitute for the actual vehicle, if a copy of the actual vehicle cannot be found.

Another approach to dimensional uncertainty is to use a range of values. This approach is demonstrated in the selection of test bullet weights ranging from 165 grains to 180 grains.

Selecting such a range of values must be based on some rationale and not just an arbitrary set of values. In the bullet weight example, the range of bullet weights was selected based on the range of bullet weights in the physical evidence.

Comparison With Other Approaches

Most of the literature available today focuses on a number of major approaches to shooting incident reconstruction.

One major approach seems to focus on data collection. Emphasis is placed upon the scientific collection of data. Providing a scientific basis for data collection is justified. However, the emphasis is on low level aspects of the shooting incident, not on the systematic evaluation of all the elements combined together to explain who, what, when, where, and how.

Another major approach provides lists of things to do. Again, most of the list elements focus on data collection and do not compose an ordered list of procedures that lead to a systematic evaluation of all the elements combined together to explain who, what, when, where, and how.

Worse yet, most crime labs do not seem to have a clue about shooting incident reconstruction. For instance, the report by the crime lab provides bullet impact information -- height above the ground, up/down angles, left/right angles. This data is called the bullet path.

Well, that characterization is true, sort of. This part of the bullet path is at the end of the trajectory. Investigators and law enforcement then claim that this is proof that the accused performed the shooting.

In reality, this data is just raw data and represents the end of the trajectory. The end of the trajectory does not connect the accused to the discharge of the firearm.

A systematic, scientific reconstruction uses straight line trajectory physics to follow a reverse trajectory to the source of the trajectory. Then, the ejection pattern of the firearm and the trajectory can be used to locate the position of the shooter. Other conditions around the area of the location of the shooter are then used to help identify the who, what, when, where, and how of the actual incident.

Bullet path information provided by the crime lab is simply the starting condition for systematic, scientific analysis and not the systematic, scientific analysis itself.

In fact, most crime labs generally do not perform shooting incident reconstructions. Under cross examination, a crime lab criminalist claimed to be an expert in shooting incident reconstruction. That person justified her qualifications by stating that she had taken a 40 hour course in shooting reconstruction. But, she further elaborated that she had only performed two reconstructions over the past five years. Given the hundreds of shooting incidents in that metropolitan area every year, two does not seem like a lot of reconstructions. This expert also stated that her crime lab generally does not perform shooting incident reconstructions.

Summary Of Basic Features

A summary of the basic features of a systematic approach is as follows:

- based on scientific principles
- uses evidence in a logical, consistent, cohesive manner
- identifies and evaluates multiple theories of the incident

- combines physical evidence, experimental data, and mathematics, science, and physics to evaluate various aspects
- employs principles, procedures, and techniques
- is repeatable by others
- based on clear and objective logic, not subjective "experience"
- clarifies using visualization such as actors, photos, videos
- justifies use of witness testimony in support of a specific theory
- justifies rebuttal of testimony inconsistent with a specific theory
- often employs anecdotal examples or analogies to help explain
- uses precise accuracy if possible, reasonableness if not possible
- properly accommodates uncertainty

Scientific and Systematic Foundations

A very clear scientific basis exists for a systematic approach to shooting incident reconstruction. The science involves deduction using bullet trajectory and stability physics and motion and force physics and induction using experimental data collection for characterizing ejection patterns and soot and stippling decay. These scientific aspects are explained in this chapter. Additionally, the systematic integration of some of these elements is also explained.

Bullet Trajectory Physics

Forces acting on a bullet in flight determine the bullet trajectory. A complete representation of these forces appears below.

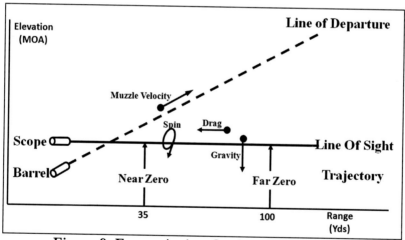

Figure 9: Forces Acting On A Bullet In Flight

An operator looks through sights (iron or riflescope) aiming the sights at the target. The line through the sights to the target is called the line of sight (LOS). In this position, the bore of the firearm is pointed slightly upwards. The line through the bore is called the line of departure (LOD).

When the firearm is discharged the bullet exits the bore along the line of departure. External forces apply to the bullet in flight. Four forces predominately effect the bullet path relative to the line of departure. **Gravity** exerts a downward force on the bullet. **Drag**, resulting from the density of air, exerts a rearward force against the front of the bullet. **Spin** imparted by the lands and grooves rotates the bullet, exercising an angular force. Finally, the **wind** exercises a force to the side or at an angle to the body of the bullet. Wind is not represented in the diagram in the above figure.

The direction of each force is indicated in the diagram using an arrow. For example, drag force is exerted in the direction of the rear of the bullet.

Physically speaking, each of these forces are resisted by an equal force in the opposite direction. These opposing forces are known as moments. With the exception of some large government agencies, most ballistics experts simply ignore the opposing forces. Testing actual bullets in flight with the equations representing the forces in the diagram has shown that ignoring the opposite forces still leads to quite accurate predictions of bullet path.

All bullets drop relative to the line of departure. Since all bullets are always dropping, a bullet cannot rise then fall. However, a bullet can be above or below the line of sight. As a result of being above and below the line of sight, bullets can have a ***practically flat path*** out to a certain distance.

Bullet locations are defined according to a specific coordinate system. This coordinate system appears in the figure below.

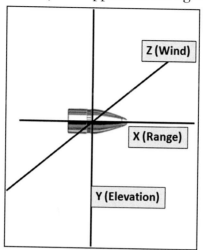

Figure 10: Bullet In Flight Coordinate System

This representation uses a 3 dimensional coordinate system. Forward movement downrange of the bullet is represented as the X coordinate. Dropping movement towards the ground is captured as the Y coordinate, called elevation. Movement to the side is called the wind coordinate, labeled with the letter Z. Thus, the location of the bullet in flight at any time is captured as the vector:

(t, X, Y, Z) = [Time (sec), X (yards), Y(inches), Z (inches)]

Measurement dimensions in each coordinate direction are represented above. For instance, time is measured in seconds. These measurement dimensions are the standard dimensions using in the trajectory physics world.

A system of differential equations describes the movement of the bullet in each of the coordinate directions. Factors that affect the movement in the various directions are coefficients in these equations. Not surprisingly, these factors include gravity, drag, and wind. Drag is dependent on the density of air, effected by temperature and pressure/altitude.

These equations of motion were derived based on the original equations of motion by Sir Isaac Newton, with the most modern extensions by ballisticians in the 1950s. A summary of the equations of motion and a reference to the originating source appears in Appendix C to this book.

Using these equations of motion, the proper coefficients, and the trajectory program MOAMaster$^{(tm)}$, developed by the author, a trajectory was predicted for the 40 Smith & Wesson used by Darren Wilson during this incident.

The first 25 yards of this predicted trajectory appears below.

Time	Range (X)	Elevation (Y)	Windage (Z)	Velocity (Vx)	Vy	Vz
sec	yds	in	in	ft/sec	ft/sec	ft/sec
0.000	0	-0.560	0	1099.999	1.813	0
0.014	5	-0.299	0	1090.391	1.359	0
0.028	10	-0.112	0	1081.099	0.904	0
0.041	15	0.001	0	1072.106	0.450	0
0.055	20	0.039	0	1063.399	-0.003	0
0.070	25	0.000	0	1054.965	-0.457	0

Table 5: 40 Smith & Wesson Trajectory, First 25 Yards

Numbers in the first four (4) columns represent the vector that characterizes the bullet trajectory, in the coordinate dimensions described earlier. Measurement dimensions are exactly as previously outlined. Since the inputs assumed no wind, the windage movement appears as zero (0) everywhere.

Velocities appear in the last three (3) columns. A velocity is the rate at which distance is changing, just like the speed of your car. The common measurement dimension for speed of a bullet in flight is feet/second as shown in the headers to the table.

This trajectory (bullet path) is for a 165 grain 40 Smith & Wesson bullet. Measurement tests have shown that this trajectory departs the muzzle of the pistol at 1100 feet/second. As the bullet travels downrange (both time and range become larger), the forward velocity drops. Forward velocity drop is the result of drag on the bullet. This reduction in forward velocity indicates that the bullet is slowing down as the bullet proceeds downrange.

This trajectory prediction has been validated many times. Trajectory validation is accomplished by placing targets at the various distances, shooting multiple cartridges, and determining the center of the impact circle. The offset between the center of the impact circle and the center of the target is compared to the Elevation(Y) at that distance. If these two offsets match, the trajectory is validated at that distance.

Validation has been accomplished many times with the predicted 40 Smith & Wesson trajectory above. Every time, the predicted trajectory and the actual trajectory perfectly match.

A better representation of this trajectory is in the form of a graph.

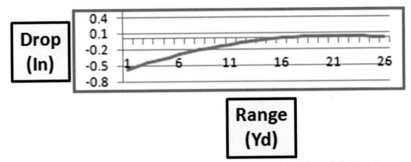

Figure 11: Sideways View Of Bullet Path, First 25 Yards

This view of the bullet path demonstrates an important principle at the core of shooting incident reconstruction. For the first 25 yards of flight, the 40 Smith & Wesson bullet trajectory is practically flat. After extensive prediction and testing, a more general principle can be stated and proved: ***bullet trajectory is practically flat for the first 25 yards, regardless of the caliber.***

At first glance, the path described above appears to be slightly curved, not flat. However, look at the actual numbers. As the bullet leaves the muzzle, the bullet path is 1/2" (0.5") below the line of sight. Proceeding down range the bullet appears to approach the line of sight, then drops slightly below the line of sight out to 25 yards. Given that the distances in most shooting incidents are short (within 10 yards) and the offset from the line of sight is 1/2" or less, this trajectory is practically flat.

Practically flat has a specific meaning -- out to 25 yards, an experienced operator can point a firearm at the center of the target and expect to impact the target within 1/2" of the center of the target. This accuracy is kill shot accuracy.

All of the shooting incident reconstructions performed in this book are at distances less than 25 yards so that this principle can be used to employ flat trajectories.

In fact, flat line trajectories are implicitly used at short distances in every text book on shooting incident reconstructions. Use of dowels and industrial quality laser pointers to represent trajectories implicitly assumes that the trajectory is flat, even if that assumption is not explicitly stated.

As the trajectory prediction for Wilson's 40 Smith & Wesson cartridge shows, at the distances between Wilson and Brown, the bullet paths were practically flat. This flat trajectory will be used in various parts of the reconstruction, including the bullet path before impact and from the location of Wilson at various times during the shooting incident.

Bullet Stability Physics

One of the forces identified that affect bullet path is spin. Spin of the bullet stabilizes the bullet in flight, so that the bullet stays on a path pointed towards the target -- moving in the direction of the line of sight.

The cause of bullet spin is the lands and grooves that compose the rifling of the barrel.

Figure 12: Rifling Composed Of Lands And Grooves

Rifling consist of parallel sets of lands and grooves down the bore of the barrel. These lands and grooves form a spiral pattern As the pressure created by the burning powder pushes the bullet down the bore of the barrel, the lands dig into the sides of the bullet. Once embedded in the sides of the bullet, these lands cause the bullet to start to spin. When the bullet exits the bore of the barrel, the bullet is spinning at a rate determined by the twist rate of the lands and grooves.

The rate of spin is determined by ammunition manufacturers based on the density of the bullet and the distribution of mass about the centerline of the bullet.

As the bullet travels downrange along the trajectory, bullet spin slows. Decrease in bullet spin is a direct result of the density of the air, just as the density of the air reduces the forward velocity of the bullet. In fact, bullet spin is actually the angular velocity of the bullet as opposed to the forward velocity. Since the density of air creates drag to slow the forward velocity, this same drag effect will cause the angular velocity to slow, reducing the spin.

Amount of spin is reflected by a number called the gyroscopic stability factor. Identification of the gyroscopic stability factor as a measure of bullet spin occurred in a published article back in the early 1900s. This factor is dimensionless having no specific units such as degrees/second. Factor values are used as relative values to compare bullet stability. A bullet with a higher stability factor is more stable.

According to the original derivation of the stability factor, as long as the factor stays above 1.1, the bullet path will remain that stable. *__A stable bullet path is one in which the path of the bullet__* *continues STRAIGHT in the same direction as the line of sight*, discussed earlier.

As might be suspected, equations exist that enable prediction of the gyroscopic stability factor as the bullet proceeds downrange. These equations are dependent upon factors such as the weight of the bullet, the spin rate of the bullet, air temperature, and air pressure. Air temperature and air pressure control the density of air which determines the amount of drag on the bullet. Thus, stability dependence on air temperature and pressure reflects the fact that the density of air and resultant drag slows the spinning, just as the density of air slows the forward motion.

These equations of stability were derived more recently, in the past few years. A summary of the equations of stability and a reference to the originating source of the equations appears in Appendix D to this book.

Using these equations of stability, the proper coefficients, and the stability program GSMaster$^{(tm)}$, developed by the author, a stability profile was predicted for the 40 Smith & Wesson used by Darren Wilson during this incident. A stability profile provides the value of the predicted stability factor as the bullet proceeds downrange from the muzzle of the firearm.

The first 25 yards of this predicted profile appears below.

Range (X) (Yds)	Velocity (Ft/Sec)	Stability Factor
0	1100	8.91
5	1090	8.88
10	1081	8.85
15	1072	8.83
20	1063	8.80
25	1054	8.78

Table 6: Stability Profile, 40 Smith & Wesson

The range from the muzzle appears in the first column. As the bullet proceeds downrange, the drag on the bullet slows the bullet. As the next column shows, the bullet speed slows. Bullet spin, which insures stability, is also affected by drag on the bullet. Column three shows that the predicted stability is reduced as the bullet flies downrange, because the drag is reducing the spinning of the bullet.

Actual decay of stability can also be shown graphically, as follows:

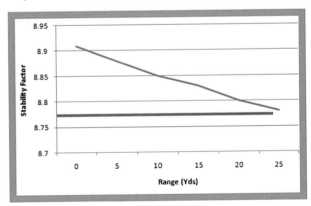

Figure 13: Gyroscopic Stability, 40 Smith & Wesson

As the graph clearly shows, the 40 Smith & Wesson bullet stability decays as the bullet moves downrange.

Because of the scale of the graph, the decay appears to be steep. In fact, the decay is quite small. Stability factor drops from 8.91 at the muzzle to 8.78 at 25 yards, a decrease of 0.001%. As long as the stability factor stays above 1.1, then the bullet is stable.

**A stable bullet path is one in which the path of the bullet continues STRAIGHT in the same direction as the line of sight.** Since the stability factor of the 40 Smith & Wesson stays well above 1.1, an obvious conclusion is that this bullet flies straight along the line of sight for the first 25 yards.

However, as with trajectory, extensive prediction and testing have demonstrated that a more general conclusion can be made regarding bullet stability. _**Bullet trajectory is straight in the same direction as the line of sight for the first 25 yards, regardless of the caliber.**_

All of the shooting incident reconstructions performed in this book are at distances less than 25 yards so that this principle can be used to employ flat and straight trajectories.

In fact, straight line trajectories that assume gyroscopic stability are implicitly used at short distances in every text book on shooting incident reconstructions. Use of dowels and industrial quality laser pointers to represent trajectories implicitly assumes that the trajectory is straight along the line of sight, even if that assumption is not explicitly stated.

As this stability prediction for Wilson's 40 Smith & Wesson cartridge shows, at the distances between Wilson and Brown, the bullet paths were straight along the line of sight. This straight assumption will be used in various parts of the reconstruction, including the bullet path before impact and the location of the Wilson at various times during the shooting incident.

Semi-Automatic Firearm Ejection Pattern

Semi-automatic firearms operate in a specific manner. An unfired cartridge is loaded into the chamber, generally cocking the hammer or the striker. The trigger is pressed by the operator, causing the hammer to fall. A falling hammer hits the firing pin, which impacts the primer of the loaded cartridge, ultimately resulting in discharge.

After discharge, the slide (on pistols) or bolt (on rifles) moves to the rear. Internal components extract and eject the fired casing.

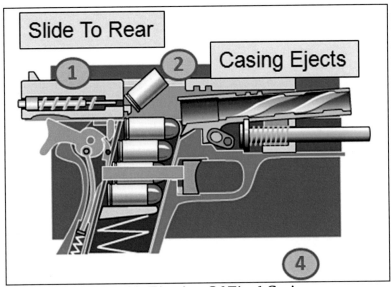

Figure 14: Ejection Of Fired Casing

Slide movement to the rear is fast and hard. So, as the fired casing ejects, the casing is thrown away from the firearm. The flight path of the ejected casing is called the ejection path.

Every time the slide cycles to load a new cartridge, the ejected casing ejection path is slight different. Differences in the shot to shot ejection path are a result of a number of factors. Each unfired cartridge has a different amount of powder due to safely allowed manufacturing tolerances. More or less powder changes the speed of slide (or bolt) movement to the rear. Different speeds yield differences in the ejection path of the fired casing. Most operators slightly vary the position of the firearm from shot to shot. This variation can also change the ejection flight path.

A group of ejected casing forms an ejection pattern on the ground. This pattern is specific to both the firearm and the ammunition discharged in the firearm.

An ejection pattern can be characterized by a number of properties.

A triangle can be formed around the ejection pattern. This triangle has a base and a centerline or height. The length of the centerline (or height) of the ejection pattern is called the ejection **distance**. Length of the base is called the **width** of the pattern.

Bullet path emanating from the shooter forms an angle with the centerline of the pattern (height of the triangle). Ejection **direction** or angle is the angle between the trajectory of the fired bullet and the centerline of the ejection pattern.

So, the ejection pattern is characterized by the features:

(D/A, D, W) = [direction(degrees), distance(ft), width(ft)].
Ejection pattern determination is inductive science. An experiment is performed. A bounding triangle is placed around the landing locations of the fired casings. (D/A, D, W) are recorded.

This data will become an important basis for incident reconstruction.

Systematic Combination Of Trajectory, Ejection

In this systematic approach, elements of the science are combined into a single framework that helps to answer the questions of who, what, when, where, and how.

At the core of this systematic approach is the combination of trajectory motion, trajectory stability and ejection pattern features.

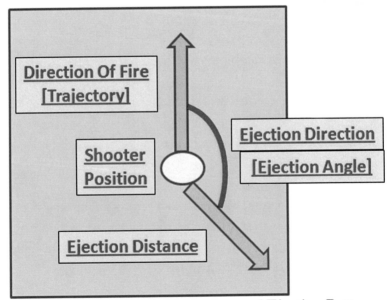

Figure 15: Systematic Trajectory and Ejection Pattern

The straight and flat trajectory is combined with the ejection direction and ejection distance. Both trajectory and ejection distance are straight lines. **A shooter is positioned at the intersection of these two straight lines.**

This approach combines the deductive science of trajectory motion and stability with the inductive science of ejection pattern determination. Combining sciences in this manner is exactly at the heart of any systematic approach.

The system of the shooting incident has 3 components -- straight and flat trajectory, shooter position, and ejection distance. These components are linked together into a shooting incident system through the ejection direction/angle.

Given the ejection direction/angle and any two of the components, the third component can be determined. Tapes, dowels, and various other aids can reconstruct the linear components of trajectory and ejection direction.

If the trajectory and the ejection direction are known, the position of the shooter can be determined. Shooter position answers the questions **"where"** and **"who"**. The shooter was standing at the determined position. Any person standing at the determined position is the shooter.

If the shooter position and the ejection direction are known, the trajectory can be determined. Trajectory determination answers the question **"how"**. A firearm possessed by the shooter was aimed in the direction of the shooter.

If the trajectory and the shooter position are known, the ejection direction can be determined. Ejection direction answers the question **"what"**. Any fired casings located in the direction of the ejection pattern came from the semi-automatic firearm used by the shooter.

In the shooting incident involving Wilson and Brown, the location of the fired casings appears in the Grand Jury evidence. Trajectories can be determined based upon the location of the first blood drops and the final body location which also appeared in the Grand Jury evidence.

Since Wilson's firearm and ammunition (for the most part) are identified in the Grand Jury evidence, the ejection pattern can be experimentally determined.

So, the scientific core of the systematic reconstruction of the Wilson/Brown incident uses ejection pattern(direction, distance, and width) to determine Wilson's shooting location(s) during the incident.

Momentum and Force Physics

During the Wilson/Brown shooting incidents, two objects were in motion. When the bullets were fired, these bullets were in motion. Whether Brown was walking or charging towards Wilson, Brown was an object in motion.

Several laws of physics are used to describe the effect when one moving object impacts another object. Any object in motion possesses momentum. Upon impact, an object in motion imparts a force to the impacted object. Physicists call this imparted force an impulse. The impacted object imparts and equal and opposite force to the impacting object called the impulse response.

Momentum and force were literally discovered by Sir Isaac Newton -- yep, the same guy who formulated the initial trajectory equations of motion.

Newton formulated a number of laws of physics that characterize objects in motion:

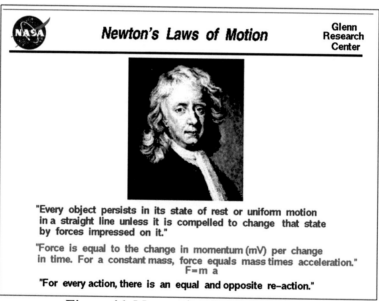

Figure 16: Newton's Laws of Motion

Law One identifies momentum - an object in uniform motion travels in a straight line unless a force compels the object to change its direction or to stop its motion.

Momentum is a great tool for comparing objects in motion. An object in motion has momentum and keeps going in the same direction as long as no force attempts to stop the motion. An object that possesses greater momentum requires an even greater force to change its straight line path. Thus, **momentum can be used to compare the ability of two objects to stay on a straight flat path prior to impact.**

Law Two informs that the force delivered by the impacting object is determined by the change in momentum over a specific period of time at impact.

This law explains that upon impact, the impacting object imparts a force to the impacted object. Therefore, **force can be used to compare the effect of various impacting objects on an impacted object.** (Just a reminder, physicists denote the force at impact as an impulse).

Law Two also provides a basic principle that is a foundation of this systematic analysis. If an object is standing still and is impacted by another object, the impacting object delivers a force. The delivered force can cause damage, destruction, or death.

Law Three indicates that the impacted object will impart an opposite force on the impacting object, changing the momentum of the impacting object. (Another reminder, physicists denote this as the impulse response.) This opposite force may not be equal due to factors such as the tensile strength of the impacted object.

Mathematical formulations are available for these laws of physics. Momentum is determined by the mass (or weight) and velocity of the moving object before impact. Force is determined by the mass, velocity, and duration of impact. The physics formulas appear in Appendix E, along with all of the other formulas.

A simple examples serves to illustrate the differences between momentum and force. A thrown hammer requires more force to deflect than a small rock. If the hammer is thrown at you, a light tap to the side simply does not deflect the hammer sufficiently to avoid being hit. A thrown small rock is far more easy to deflect away from you. The thrown hammer has more momentum than the small rock. If the thrown hammer impacts, the damage can be extensive, even death. However, if the thrown small rock impacts, then the damage is likely to be limited to a bruise. Clearly, a thrown hammer delivers greater force to the impacted object than a thrown small rock.

Now, consider two bullets in comparison -- the 308 Winchester rifle bullet (a hammer) and the 45 ACP pistol bullet (a small rock).

Object	Bullet Weight (grains)	Impact Weight (lbs)	Muzzle Velocity (ft/sec)	Impact Velocity (ft/sec)	Momentum At Impact (lb ft/sec)	Force At Impact (lb ft/sec^2)	Force At Impact (Newtons)
45 ACP	230	.033	850	798	26	13167	1820
308 Win	168	.024	2640	2461	59	29532	4082

Table 7: Momentum and Force Comparison, 308 Win, 45 ACP

Impact velocities at 100 yards in this table are computed by MOAMaster[tm], the same computer program developed by the author to compute the 40 Smith & Wesson trajectory displayed earlier. Force depends on the amount of time during which the impact occurs. For this analysis, the **first 2 milliseconds** are used as the amount of time in the force two calculations. The first two milliseconds are the time period in which the maximum impact force is delivered to the impacted object. After this first two milliseconds, the equal and opposite force starts to significantly reduce the forward velocity of the bullet, reducing the force that is applied by the impacting bullet.

A 308 Win bullet is lighter that a 45 ACP bullet. However, this 308 Win possesses far greater velocity/speed than the 45 ACP. When weight and velocity at impact are combined into momentum, the far greater velocity of the 308 Win more than compensates for the smaller weight of the bullet.

In comparison, the 308 Win possesses 2.24 (59/26) more momentum at 100 yards. This greater momentum means that 2.24 more greater force is required to move the 308 Win off the straight and flat bullet path. Since more force is required to cause the 308 Win to deviate from the straight and flat bullet path, the 308 Win is called a "high power" round.

At impact at 100 yards, the 308 Win also imparts 2.24 (4082/1820) times more force against a target than the 45 ACP during the first 2 milliseconds of impact. Since the 308 Win is represents the moving hammer while the 45 ACP represents the small rock, this result should make sense.

As part of the reconstruction, the ejection pattern of Wilson's firearm with Wilson's ammunition needs to be determined, as described some pages ago. Unfortunately, the summary of Wilson's ammunition in the Grand Jury evidence is incomplete. So, momentum is employed to select reasonable ammunition substitutes for Wilson's ammunition. Momentum is used to compare possible ammunition alternatives, since momentum is the measure to compare the capability to maintain a straight and flat trajectory. **<u>Two bullets of the same caliber with equal momentum at the muzzle possess the same capability to maintain the same flat and straight bullet trajectory</u>.**

Another evaluation during the reconstruction compares the effect of Brown's potential impact with Wilson with the impact of a 308 bullet in flight. For this comparison, the amount of force imparted during the 2 milliseconds after impact. provides a fair comparison of the amount of force delivered by each impacting object. Limiting the analysis to the first 2 milliseconds is called an instantaneous evaluation for comparison purposes.

Potential effect of Brown's impact into Wilson's body is not calculated. The impulse response (equal and opposite force) of Wilson's body is a very complex process, difficult to calculate directly. However, the effect of the impact on Wilson's body can be illustrated by using an analogous situation. One of the enumerated features of this systematic approach is to use analogy or example if necessary and useful.

Determining Wound Path From A Medical Report

A trajectory is one of the components of the system approach outline above. In the case of a body, bullet path through the body indicates the final section of the trajectory of the bullet.

In cases where death occurs, a medical report is prepared by a medical examiner, sometimes identified as a coroner. This report characterizes the wound path through the body. In this section, a summary is provided of the most typical approaches to bullet path characterization.

If a bullet path in the body has both an entrance and an exit wound, the location of these wounds are provided. On the other hand, if the path has only an entrance wound, then location of this wound is provided, along with an impact angle relative to one of the body planes defined in the medical community.

All wound locations are identified relative to common reference points, such as the top of the head and the anterior or posterior midline of the body. An anterior midline is down the front and center of the body. Similarly, a posterior midline is down the back and center of the body. Generally, diagrams are also provided as a visual aid to help identify the wound locations.

An example of an entrance and exit wound specification, including diagram and description is as follows:

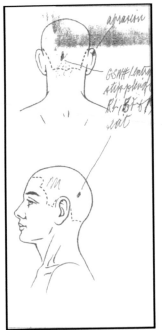

Entrance:	5 ¾" Below Top Of Head	
	¾" To Left Of Midline	
Exit:	4 ¾" Below Top Of Head	
	2 ¾" To Left Of Midline	

Figure 17: Typical Entrance, Exit Wound Specification

The entrance wound is identified by a red rectangle. A blue rectangle identifies the exit wound. Both wound locations are specified by an offset from the top of the head. Both wound locations are also identified by an offset from the posterior midline of the body.

This specific approach comes from high school geometry and is called a two point specification of a line. With two clearly identified points on the body, the line that represents the bullet path through the body is easily determined.

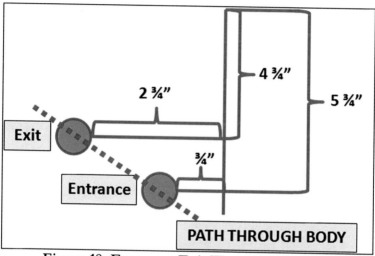

Figure 18: Entrance, Exit Wound Body Path

Finding a wound location is easily accomplished. Place a metal plate against the top of the head, measure down along the midline, then move perpendicularly across from the midline. Place a marker at that location. Repeat for both the entrance and the exit wounds. With the proper tools and these marked locations, a visualization of the bullet path can be replicated on another person.

Using the entrance wound and the exit wound to construct a straight line bullet path through the body assumes that nothing in the body deflected the bullet during its transition through the body. Generally speaking, if the bullet path was deflected inside the body, the medical report clearly identifies the deflection. A statement appears in the report, such as "the bullet impacted the right hip, angled upward, proceeded through the lung, impacted the 8th rib, angled to the right, and exited the body." If the report does not indicate any deflection in the bullet path, the bullet path is straight. An example of an entrance wound and impact angle specification, including diagram and description is as follows:

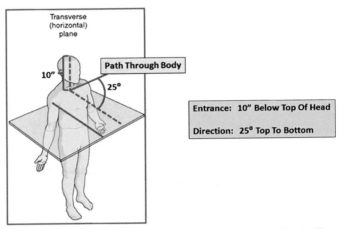

Figure 19: Entrance Wound, Impact Angle Body Path

In this representation, the entrance wound is specified by an offset from the top of the head. If necessary, an offset from the anterior or posterior midline would also be employed to locate the entrance wound. An angle is also provided. In this example, the angle is relative to transverse or horizontal plane of the body. This plane is parallel to the ground, assuming that the body is standing straight.

This specific approach also derives from high school geometry and is called a point and angle specification of a line. With a clearly identified point on the body and an angle from a specific body plane, the line that represents the bullet path through the body is easily determined.

Finding the entrance wound location is easily accomplished, as described above. Place a metal plate against the top of the head, measure down along the midline, then move perpendicularly across from the midline, if necessary. Place a marker at that location.

Using a protractor, the angle can be measured relative to the indicated plane. With the proper equipment, a dowel can be fastened at the entrance wound location and oriented at the angle relative to the indicated plane. As a result, the wound path through the body can be replicated on another human.

As with the two point form of the body wound path specification, if the report does not indicate any deflection in the bullet path, the bullet path is straight.

A number of important points should be made here. Simple high school geometry is being used to indicate the bullet path through the body. Detailed medical knowledge is unnecessary. Occasionally, as will be discussed shortly, some anatomical terms may need definition. Anyone with a high school biology course, and an anatomy book can determine the definition and its meaning for location purposes.

These geometric bullet path locations from common reference points are the foundation for constructing a bullet path through the body. This path construction takes place on the surface of the body, not by penetrating the body. Therefore, detailed medical knowledge is just unnecessary.

Two medical examiners were involved in identifying bullet paths in the body. An Autopsy Report was created by the St. Louis County

Medical Examiner. A second Autopsy Report was written by Dr. Michael Baden, an independent Medical Examiner hired by the Brown family. Both of these reports explicitly identify the bullet paths through the body. Key bullet paths through the body identified by the St. Louis County Medical Examiner have already been summarized.

These key bullet paths are employed during the reconstruction to evaluate the alternate theories of the incident. Using these bullet paths through the body to determine the body position of Brown and the location and body position of Officer Wilson helps to answer the questions of **"where"** and **"how"**. In order to answer these questions, the bullet paths in the body are combined with the straight and flat bullet paths determined for the Officer Wilson's 40 Smith & Wesson pistol. This combination of bullet path in the body and bullet path from the pistol is another example of the systematic basis of this analysis.

Summary of Scientific and Systematic Basis

In this chapter, the scientific laws, the principles derived from those laws specific to this incident, and the systematic combination of some of those laws and principles have been clearly identified:

- Bullet trajectory is practically flat for the first 25 yards, regardless of the caliber.

- Bullet trajectory is straight in the same direction as the line of sight for the first 25 yards, regardless of the caliber.

- Ejection pattern forms a triangle that is characterized by direction/angle, distance, and width.

- A shooter is positioned at the intersection of trajectory and ejection distance -- two straight lines.

- The system of a shooting incident has 4 components -- straight and flat trajectory, shooter position, ejection distance, and ejection direction.

- Given the ejection direction/angle and any two of the components, the third component can be determined.

- Momentum can be used to compare the ability of two objects to stay on the same straight flat path prior to impact.

- Force can be used to compare the effect of various impacting objects on an impacted object.

- Two cartridges of the same caliber with the same momentum possess equivalent capability to sustain the same straight and flat bullet path.

- Simple high school geometry is used to specify the path of a bullet through the body.

- An entry wound and exit wound body path description is the two point specification of a line in simple geometry.

- An entry wound and impact angle body path description is the point angle specification of a line in simple geometry.

- A medical degree is NOT required to use the geometric specifications of a bullet path in a body for reconstruction.

Initial Grand Jury Evidence Analysis

Several very specific elements of the Grand Jury provide important information necessary to perform the shooting reconstruction.

Locations of various elements of physical evidence are provided in the Grand Jury evidence. A location map for these pieces of evidence was shown earlier.

Distance Moved By Brown During The Incident

Using the locations, some important distances can be identified.

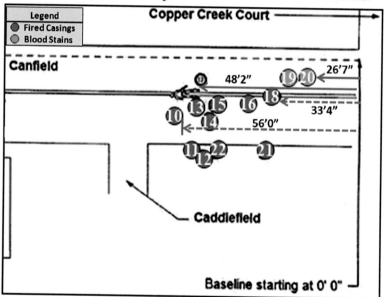

Figure 20: Distances Determined From Evidence Locations

Indicator 20 identifies the location of the first blood drops. Distance from the baseline to these first blood drops is 26' 7". According to the evidence location table, presented earlier, distance from the baseline to the left foot of Brown's body on the ground was 48' 2". By subtracting the two distances, the distance Brown moved after turning can be determined. **Brown moved 21' 7" from the turning location to the final position of his body on the ground**. This distance is about 7 yards of movement after Brown turned.

Clearly, Brown moved towards Wilson and not the other way around. The first blood spots were on the East side of the road. The final location of the body was 21'7" to the West. The head of the body was towards the west, according to the Autopsy Report.

This distance is also significant. If Brown had been slowly walking with his hands in the air or shot just after he turned towards Wilson, the distance between the first blood drops and the body would have been far less. Thus, **this fairly long distance indicates that Brown was moving at a fast rate of movement, not walking**.

Distance Moved By Wilson During The Incident

This same location information provides insight into the distance moved by Wilson during the instance.

Locations of fired casings bound the ejection patterns created by Wilson's pistol during the shooting incident. As the evidence location summary shows, the first casing from the reference line was found 33' 4" from the reference line. Location of the last casing was 56' 0" from the reference line. Subtracting these distances determines that **Wilson moved 22' 8" from the start of the incident when Brown turned towards Wilson to the end of the incident**, when Brown lay face down on the ground. As with Brown, this distances is somewhat more than 7 yards.

As with Brown, this distance is a fairly long distance. From this distance, two conclusions can be determined. **Wilson and Brown moved about the same distance. Furthermore, Wilson moved in the same direction as Brown, NOT towards each other**.

If Wilson had moved towards Brown instead of away from Brown, the shooting distance would have been smaller. As a result, the first and last cases would have been much closer together, much closer.

Moreover, Wilson could NOT have been standing over Brown, executing Brown. In that situation, all of the cases would have been in a fairly tight pattern that matched a **single** ejection pattern of Wilson's pistol. These issues will be evaluated in detail later.

Medical Examiner Report Wound Specification

Previously, several techniques used by medical examiners to locate wounds using simple geometry were demonstrated. While those techniques are the most effective, being the easiest to reconstruct, the St. Louis County Medical Examiner chose a different approach.

In the Autopsy Report created by the Medical Examiner, two specific reference points were utilized: the anterior midline of the head and the external auditory meatus.

Anterior means front. Anterior midline of the head travels down the center of the front of the head.

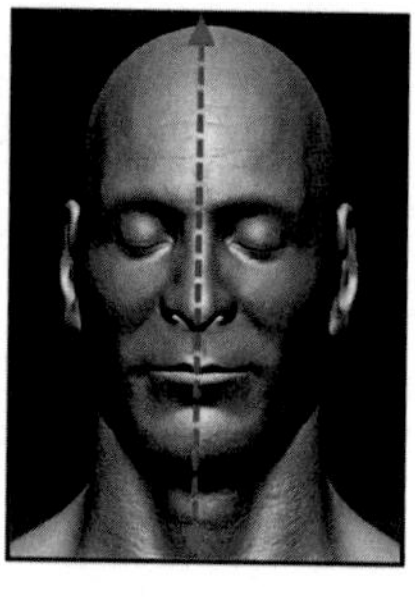

Figure 21: Anterior Midline of the Head

In the figure above, the dashed red arrow clearly identifies the anterior midline of a male head.

As the second reference for wound location identification, the medical examiner uses the location "level of the external auditory meatus". A quick reference to pretty much **ANY** anatomy and physiology text book reveals the following diagram:

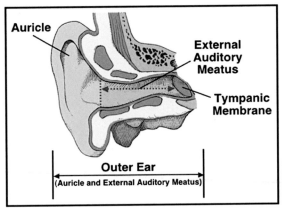

Figure 22: External Auditory Meatus Identification

No medical magic here either. Simple biology requiring only the knowledge to read a diagram, not even high school biology is necessary. The terminology sounds scientific (and is) **BUT**, this location is nothing more than the middle of the ear canal. A medical degree is not necessary to identify this location on the human body. Find the opening in the ear. Locate the middle of that opening. Special medical knowledge is just not necessary.

<u>**Anyone can identify these two locations on any human body without any special medical knowledge.**</u> This statement is not an attempt to criticize the medical examiner for using these terms. In fact, the examiner is correct to use these terms. These terms are

the commonly accepted terms for anatomically describing these locations.

This comment is a criticism of those individuals who have claimed that only a person with a medical degree can understand the meaning of these terms and identify these locations on the body of another human. This belief is total nonsense.

An example of the usage of these two references to locate a wound appears below:

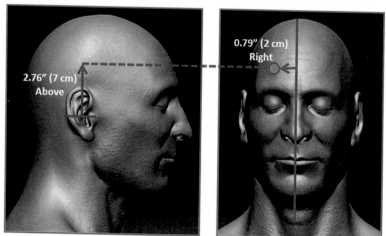

Figure 23: Wound Location Using Reference Locations

This illustration did **NOT** appear in the St Louis County Medical Examiner's Autopsy Report. Rather, the author created this diagram to illustrate the process of using a wound location specified in the Medical Examiner's Report.

Wound Number 2 was identified in the Medical Examiner's Report as follows:

2. There is a gunshot entrance wound of the central forehead. This wound is located 7.0 cm above the level of the right external auditory meatus and 2.0 cm right of the anterior midline of the head.

Translated into English units, this description becomes:

> **#2. There is a gunshot wound of the central forehead. This wound is located 2.76" above the level of the right external auditory meatus and 0.79" right of the anterior midline of the head.**

Source: St. Louis County Medical Examiner's Autopsy Report

This description can be used to locate the described wound on the head of another person. Look back at the figure above. In the image on the left, find the right external auditory meatus. In the image on the right, find the anterior centerline of the face. Just in case, these reference locations are clearly marked.

Follow these steps in the left and right images above. Place a tape down the midline of the head. Find the level of the right external auditory meatus(center of the ear hole). Move 2.76" straight up from the level of the external auditory meatus. Place a marker at that location. Wrap a tape around the side of the head, starting from the marker, maintaining that same distance above the external auditory meatus, moving towards the face. Keep wrapping the tape around the face towards the anterior midline of the head. When the side tape crosses the midline tape, hold the side tape in place. Then, measure 0.79" back to the left. Place another marker. This marker is the location of the wound.

Moving back to left after the tapes cross is necessary because the wound is to the right of the midline of the head. That reference is to the right of the body of the victim, not to the right of the body of the person performing the measurement.

In the figure, a dashed red line crosses from the right side of the head to the front side of the head. This dashed line represents the side tape described above that moves from the side across the forehead towards the anterior midline.

This process may seem a bit cumbersome to follow. If you felt that way as you tried to follow the process, you would be correct. This approach to wound location simply is not as clear and precise as the two approaches outlined earlier. However, this approach certainly provides enough detailed information to be able to locate the wound on any human body of similar proportions.

Guidelines For Reading Autopsy Reports

In reading an autopsy or other medical report, detailed knowledge of every anatomical term for the human body is not necessary. An understanding of the immediate terms being referenced is all that is necessary. For instance, in the Medical Examiner's report in this case, the only element of the ear that needs definition is the term "external auditory meatus". All of the remaining elements of the ear are totally irrelevant for reading this report for wound locations.

Even terms such as the "bullet came to rest just below the 8th right rib" are easily located with a diagram.

HINT: Try using the Google search engine. Diagrams of most anatomical elements are easily found and located on the body using those diagrams, without special medical knowledge.

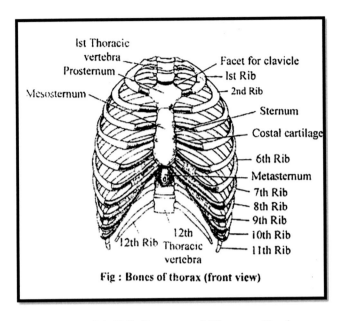

Fig : Bones of thorax (front view)

Figure 24: Rib Layout of Human Body

This front (or anterior) diagram clearly shows the location of the
8th rib. Even a course in basic biology is unnecessary to determine
the location of the 8th rib. The 8th rib starts right at the bottom of
the sternum, moves downward to a point several inches below the
sternum, then begins an upward path towards the backbone. A
posterior view not shown) reveals that the 8th rib terminates at a
location approximately across from the starting location at the
bottom of the sternum. At this point, the only information needed
to identify the location of the resting place of the bullet is a
definition of the location and path of the 8th rib. All of the other
ribs and other elements of the rib cage, such as the facet for the
clavicle, are irrelevant for location of this bullet resting place.

Summary Of Initial Analysis Results

A number of important conclusions have been obtained in this first analysis of the Grand Jury evidence. These results are as follows:

- Brown moved 21' 7" from the turning location to the final position of his body on the ground.

- Brown moved from East to West, towards Officer Wilson.

- This fairly long distance indicates that Brown was moving at a fast rate of movement, not walking.

- Wilson moved 22' 8" from the start of the incident when Brown turned towards Wilson to the end of the incident

- Wilson and Brown moved about the same distance.

- Wilson moved in the same direction as Brown, NOT towards each other .

- The Autopsy Report used two specific reference points to identify wound locations: the anterior midline of the head and the external auditory meatus.

- Anyone can identify these two locations on any human body without any special medical knowledge.

Ejection Pattern Determination

In this case, the ejection pattern is an important element of the reconstruction. So, an ejection pattern experiment was performed. The goal of this experiment is precisely to determine the ejection direction/angle, the ejection distance, and the ejection width.

Ejection pattern determination is an example of inductive science. An experiment is performed. This experiment provides specific data. Based on the specific data, general conclusions are stated regarding the ejection pattern for the class of pistol used and the brand of ammunition employed. Extending from the specific to the general is the basis of inductive science.

Selection Of Firearm and Ammunition

If access to the actual firearm in the incident is possible, obviously, this firearm should be used for the ejection pattern determination. Access to the pistol owned by Officer Wilson was not practical at this point. So, a substitute pistol was utilized.

Figure 25: Actual Sig Sauer P-220 Used In Experiment

113

For the most part, any copy of a firearm of the same manufacturer and model can be used in an ejection pattern study.

This statement is particularly true if the firearm is possessed by a law enforcement officer. Law enforcement departments have polices that pretty much require an officer to use a firearm that is configured exactly as the firearm is issued from the manufacturer. Very little if any modifications or enhancements are generally allowed to a duty weapon possessed by a law enforcement officer. This restriction is usually imposed for both reliability and liability reasons. In fact, all maintenance on officer duty firearms is generally performed by a departmental employee called an Armorer. The Armorer has taken training from the manufacturer and is certified to return that firearm to factory specification.

Using a different Sig Sauer P-229 in this case is more than justified. In the Armorer training course offered by Sig Sauer, huge emphasis is placed on the interchangeability of parts for a specific model of pistol. All of the parts of the P-229 are interchangeable without custom fitting being required. Some other firearms, such as the 1911 models, require extensive custom fitting, so that parts are not generally interchangeable, for the most part.

Interchangeability of parts in the Sig Sauer product line is emphasized in the Armorer training offered by Sig Sauer to law enforcement armorers. Sig Sauer offers a course that addresses maintenance, diagnosis and repair of their Classic Line Pistols. This course covers the P220, P226, P228, P229 and P239 pistol models. The final exam in this course specifically emphasizes the interchangeability of parts for each specific model, such as the P229. Each student is given a copy of the same pistol model, for example, the P220. The firearms are disassembled. All of the parts, except the frame and the slide, are thrown into a giant box. The frame and slide are retained by the student. A tremendous shaking is given to the box containing the parts from all of the pistols. The class has a time limit to sort the parts and re-assemble the pistols into full functionality. Since all of the parts from all of the pistols of that model are interchangeable, the student does not need to identify the parts that came from his specific pistol. Interchangeable parts simply means that the student only has to find a copy of the parts needed to assemble the pistol.

Interchangeability of parts in this situation assures that using another copy of the Sig Sauer P-229 yields a comparable ejection pattern to the pattern of Wilson's pistol.

Selection of ammunition for ejection pattern testing is a bit more complicated in this case. As shown in the Grand Jury evidence, the specific ammunition used by Wilson during the incident can be characterized as follows:

- Darren Wilson utilized Federal cartridges with bullet weights ranging from 158 grain to 180 grain in weight

The Grand Jury evidence also shows that Wilson used jacketed hollow point (JHP) ammunition. Federal manufactures a wide range of brands that meet these specifications in caliber 40 Smith & Wesson.

Searching through the Federal catalog for 40 Smith & Wesson ammunition that ranges from 158 grain to 180 grain revealed the following brands of ammunition, among others:

Figure 26: Comparable Brands of Federal Ammunition

Federal also manufactures this same Range Target Practice brand with a bullet weight of 150 grains.

Evaluating comparable ammunition can be accomplished by using momentum. Recall that:

- Two cartridges of the same caliber with the same momentum possess equivalent capability to sustain the same straight and flat bullet path.

For momentum comparison purposes, a several brands of Federal Smith & Wesson ammunition that use a JHP bullet were selected from the Federal offerings. These cartridges would be typical of the brand of Federal cartridge used by Wilson. Since the exact brand of Wilson's Federal JHP ammunition was not provided, these cartridges represent reasonable alternatives.

Sometimes obtaining the exact ammunition is difficult, so that alternative brands must be considered, preferably by the same manufacturer. In this case, the Federal 40 Smith & Wesson Range Target Practice ammunition was selected as the potential alternatives. This brand of ammunition was selected because the brand provides bullets in the same bullet weight ranges as described in the Grand Jury Evidence.

Momentum calculations for the candidate JHP ammunition appear in the table below:

Manufacturer	Type	Weight (gr)	Weight (lbs)	Muzzle Velocity (ft/sec)	Momentum (lb ft/sec)
Federal	JHP	155	0.022	1140	25.25
Federal	JHP	165	0.024	980	23.10
Federal	JHP	180	0.026	1000	25.71

Table 8: Federal 40 Caliber JHP Momentum Calculations

Momentum calculations for test FMJ ammunition appear in the table below:

Manufacturer	Type	Weight (gr)	Weight (lbs)	Muzzle Velocity (ft/sec)	Momentum (lb ft/sec)
Federal	FMJ	165	0.024	1050	24.75
Federal	FMJ	180	0.026	985	25.32

Table 9: Federal 40 Caliber FMJ Momentum Calculations

An FMJ alternative cartridge with a 150 grain bullet was not considered as test ammunition. This bullet weight is too small for the range of bullet weights used by Wilson. The 165 grain alternative cartridge is somewhat larger in weight than the smallest bullet located in the Physical Evidence Map found in the Grand Jury Evidence. However, the somewhat larger weight generally provides better indicators of the ejection pattern dimensions.

The 165 grain JHP cartridge possesses slightly lower momentum at the muzzle than the 165 grain FMJ cartridge. This difference of 24.75 versus 23.1 lb ft / sec is about 6.6% difference in momentum. This percentage difference is not particularly significant, well within a reasonable level of error.

117

Similarly, the 180 grain JHP cartridge also exhibits slightly lower momentum at the muzzle than the 180 grain FMJ cartridge. This difference of 25.32 compared to 25.71 represents about 1.5% difference in momentum. This percentage difference is pretty much negligible.

These small differences in momentum between the JHP cartridges and the FMJ cartridges justify the use of the 165 grain and 180 grain Range Target Practice ammunition for ejection pattern determination.

As the momentum calculations clearly show, in this case, usage of a JHP bullet is unnecessary for purposes of ejection pattern testing. The bullet type does not affect the flight characteristics of the bullet.

Bullet type does affect the wound ballistics -- the wounding behavior of the bullet as the bullet tears through tissue. Three major categories of bullets generally exist: unjacketed, full metal jacket (FMJ) and jacketed hollow point (JHP). Each of these bullet types behaves differently when passing through human tissue.

Unjacketed bullets **fragment**, breaking into multiple pieces of metal of various sizes. These bullets inflict the most damage as the pieces spread out and tear. FMJ bullets **remain intact**. The jacket pretty much holds the internal bullet intact, with potentially small amounts of deformation. When passing through tissue, these bullets create the smallest hole and permanent damage to the tissue. However, these bullets penetrate the deepest, increasing the likelihood that important organs, such as the heart, will be damaged. Finally, the FMJ bullets **expand**. As a result of the expansion, the bullets create a bigger hole. However, the expanded bullet exposes a greater cross sectional area to the surrounding tissue. As a result, the tissues create greater drag, reducing the penetration depth. A reduced penetration depth reduces the likelihood of that an important organ will be penetrated, with less potential stopping power for the bullet.

Ejection Pattern Testing

An ejection pattern test was conducted using the firearm and the ammunition described above.

A simple but effective ejection pattern testing area was established on a private shooting range facility.

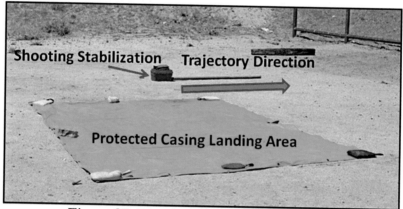

Figure 27: Ejection Pattern Testing Area

This simple setup achieves two important objectives. The shooting direction is reasonably repeatable. Fired casings do not get mixed in with other fired casings on the range.

A steel rod is laid on the ground to identify the shot-shot trajectory direction. A stabilized shooting platform is created using a toolbox. By using tape on the toolbox, the firearm is consistently placed in

119

the same shooting location. Placing the shooting hand on the toolbox in the same location as marked by the tape and aiming along the steel rod provides reasonable shot-shot, shooting direction repeatability.

Other equipment such as a Ransom Rest could certainly be utilized to obtain more accurate repeatability. However, human shooters don't generally achieve perfect shot-shot repeatability. Part of the ejection pattern during an actual shooting incident is determined by human variations in shooting technique. This approach provides reasonable repeatability but at the same time allows for small amounts of human variability during the actual incident.

While the range was a private range, previous users have deposited a large number of other fired casings. Using a tarp to create a landing area protects the integrity of the fired casings and their locations during this test. The tarp is held in location by a set of rocks and/or sandbags around the edges. None of the fired casings impacted any of the rocks. Rock impacts would have caused the fired casings to ricochet, yielding inaccurate results for the pattern.

The tarp is made of a plastic/canvas type material. Using this material has an added benefit. The fired casings do not roll after landing. Each casings stays exactly where the casing landed.

Ejection Pattern Testing Shooting Protocol

As demonstrated earlier, two ammunition weights were selected for usage in the ejection pattern testing. These bullet weights were chosen as representative of the bullet weights found at the location of the incident.

An equal number of cartridges with each bullet weight were used during the actual ejection pattern testing. The actual shooting test was performed using 10 unfired cartridges with the 165 grain bullet and 10 unfired cartridges with the 180 grain bullet.

An equal number of cartridges of each weight were chosen to insure that neither of the bullet weights would bias the results in a specific direction.

All 20 of the unfired cartridges were used in a single combined test. This approach was employed because this approach represents the actual shooting incident situation. Officer Wilson discharged a mixture of cartridges of different weights in a single incident.

Ejection Pattern Testing Results

After all 20 shots are discharged, the ejection area is explicitly marked.

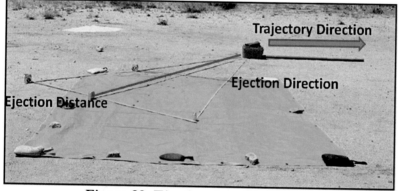

Figure 28: Ejection Area Identified

Locking tape measures are used to mark the boundaries of the ejection area. The side boundaries are determined by the location of the fired casing that fell the greatest distance in that direction. A base boundary is determined by the fired casing that moved the greatest distance from the shooting location. The ejection area boundaries form a natural triangle.

After the boundaries are identified, a separate locking tape measure is used to determine the centerline of the ejection area. Since the base of the triangle is marked with a tape measure, the center location of the base is easily determined. A triangle centerline tape is placed between the center of the triangle base and the shooting position.

After the boundaries and centerline of the ejection area have been determined using locking tapes, the ejection area parameters are measured. Ejection direction/angle is measured by using a protractor to determine the angle between the trajectory line (direction of fire) and the centerline down the center of the ejection area triangle. Minimum distance case is the distance from the shooting position to the location of the first fired casing in the ejection area. Ejection distance is the measured distance between the firing position location and the base of the triangle along the triangle centerline. Ejection width is the length of the base between the two sides of the triangle. Distances are easily determined by reading the locked tape measures.

Ejection Pattern Testing Results

The measured values for the ejection pattern specification are shown below.

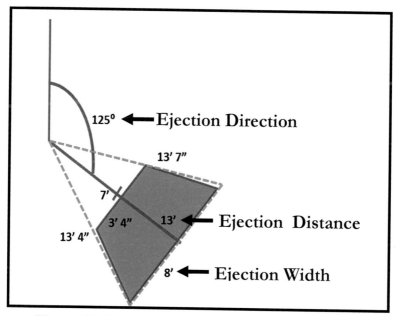

Figure 29: Measured Ejection Pattern Dimensions

All ejected casings flew to the right and to the rear. Ejection direction is 125°. Ejection distance is 13'. Ejection pattern width is 8' at the ejection distance. Every P-229 ejection pattern with similar ammunition as used by Wilson covers a triangle 8' wide at the base and 13' high at the centerline. These dimensions can be utilized to divide a large group of fired casings into ejection pattern areas. Multiple ejection pattern areas determine the multiple locations of a shooter, if impact locations are known, as explained in the section on scientific and systematic basis.

Accommodating Uncertainty

Several elements of this test reflect potential uncertainty. Ammunition with two separate bullet weights is used. An equal

123

number of discharges of each of the bullet weights were used to prevent a specific bullet weight from distorting the results in favor of one bullet weight over another. All discharges were hand fired, not fired from a machine rest, reflecting the uncertainty behind the shooting technique of a typical operator. The resultant measurements reflect the combination of these sources of uncertainty. This combination is appropriate for the specific incident under investigation.

Comparison With Other Pattern Studies

In some cases, the effects of each source of uncertainty upon ejection pattern are an important aspect of the case. In those cases, a more formal experimental approach is used. Experimental variables are defined. A range of values is determined for each variable. An ejection pattern test is performed for each combination of variable values. The resultant ejection patterns are summarized in a single table.

Here is an example summary table for ejection pattern evaluation where a specific source of uncertainty is evaluated:

Experimental Variable	Test	Manufacturer	Brand	Bullet Weight	Muzzle Velocity
Baseline Bullet, Velocity Lightest Bullet Lowest Muzzle Velocity	AMERICAN EAGLE 9mm LUGER	Federal	Eagle	124 gr	1000 ft/sec
Same Size Bullet Faster Muzzle Velocity	CORBON 9mm Luger+P 125 gr JHP	Corbon	9mm +P	125 gr	1250 ft/sec
Much Heavier Bullet Same Muzzle Velocity	FIOCCHI 9mm LUGER 147 GRS. FMJ	Fiocci	9mm	147 gr	1050 ft/sec

Table 10: Experimental Example, Ejection Pattern Testing

In this example, the experimental variable is the combination of bullet size and muzzle velocity of a 9mm cartridge. Three combinations of bullet weight and muzzle velocity represent the range of values for the experimental variable. For instance, the baseline combination of bullet weight and muzzle velocity is Federal Eagle ammunition. This ammunition uses a 124 grain bullet, which is the lightest weight bullet of the three ammunition types. This cartridge also exhibits a muzzle velocity of 1000 ft/sec, also the lowest muzzle velocity across the test ammunition. All other bullet weight/muzzle velocity combinations use heavier bullets or faster muzzle velocities.

The same test firearm was used for all 3 tests, a Glock 17. Each test consisted of a discharge of 10 cartridges, generally a sufficient number to accommodate other sources of variations, such as operator technique in hold the pistol in the same position from shot-shot.

The table contains the ejection pattern results for each of the ejection pattern tests using the same procedure as outlined previously. From the specific data in this table, some general conclusions can be made regarding 9mm ammunition when used with a Glock 17. Ejection direction (angle) ranges from 125° to 130°. Ejection distance ranges from about 7' to 12'. Ejection width ranges from 1' 7" to 3' 10".

Comparing the two entries with approximately the same bullet weight, a higher muzzle velocity results in a larger ejection distance. The higher muzzle velocity results in faster slide movement to the rear. Faster slide movement to the rear imparts greater force to the ejector. The equal and opposite greater force from the ejector back to the casing throws the casings a greater distance.

Two of the entries possess approximately the same muzzle velocity. The bullet with a higher weight results in a shorter ejection distance. A heavier bullet results in a slower rearward movement of the slide. This slower rearward movement of the slide imparts lesser force to the ejector. The equal and opposite lesser force to the casing throws the casings a shorter distance.

These last few paragraphs clearly demonstrate the inductive approach to science. Empirical data was collected from specific tests. Based on this specific test data, general physical behavior was deduced.

Interestingly, the results of this experiment compare favorably with other ejection pattern experiments. In this experiment, ejection direction (angle) ranges from 125° to 130°. Ejection distance ranges from about 7' to 12'. Using the Wilson's type pistol and ammunition, the ejection direction (angle) was 125° and the ejection distance was 13'. Wilson's ejection pattern is for a Sig Sauer P-229 pistol using 40 Smith & Wesson ammunition. The testing in the experiment above was for a Glock 17 pistol using 9mm ammunition. Clearly, the pistols and ammunition calibers are completely different. Yet, the resultant measurements are comparable.

Many other pistol ejection patterns tend to fall within these ranges. Ejection area widths do vary quite a bit. In the experiment above, ejection area width ranged from 1' 7" to 3' 10". Wilson's ejection area width was a whopping 8'. Since the above tests are for the 9mm cartridge and Wilson's test was for the 40 Smith & Wesson, a reasonable inference might be that the cartridge caliber has the greatest effect on ejection area width. This effect could be easily tested with a controlled experiment using cartridge caliber as the experimental variable!

Summary And Conclusions

The important statements from this section are as follows:

- For the most part, any copy of a firearm of the same manufacturer and model can be used in an ejection pattern study.

- Interchangeability of parts in this situation assures that using another copy of the Sig Sauer P-229 yields a comparable ejection pattern.

- Federal 40 Smith & Wesson Range Target Practice brand of ammunition was selected because the brand provides bullets in the same bullet weight ranges as described in the Grand Jury Evidence.

- Small differences in momentum between the JHP cartridges and the FMJ cartridges justify the use of the 165 grain and 180 grain Range Target Practice ammunition for ejection pattern determination.

- Ejection direction is 125°. Ejection distance is 13'. Ejection pattern width is 8' at the ejection distance.

- Every ejection pattern covers a triangle 8' wide at the base and 13' high at the centerline.

Shooting Distance Determination

According to the Autopsy Report by the St. Louis County, none of the wounds exhibited soot or stippling. Using this fact, the minimum distance from which Wilson was shooting every time the firearm was discharged can be determined.

An experiment was performed to determined the distance at which soot and stippling no longer appears on a target. This kind of experiment is another example of inductive science, where a specific experiment leads to a general conclusion about the disappearance of soot and stippling. These results are specific to the type of firearm and the type of ammunition. Evidence collected in this experimentation manner is called empirical evidence.

Selection Of Firearm and Ammunition

This experiment was performed with the same firearm used to determine the ejection pattern for Wilson's pistol, a Sig Sauer P-229. However, only one type of ammunition was used.

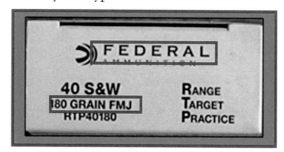

Figure 30: Shooting Distance Test Ammunition

Typically, a heavier bullet uses more gunpowder. So, the heaver bullet was selected for this test to provide the maximum shooting distance at which soot and stippling would disappear.

Discharge Experimental Protocol

In order to determine the distance at which soot and stippling disappear, a simple discharge approach is used.

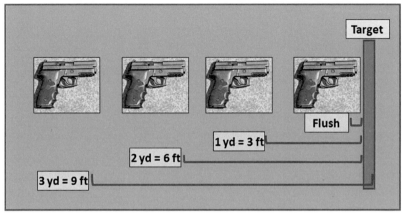

Figure 31: Soot and Stippling Discharge Protocol

The basis for the discharge protocol is the distance between the muzzle and the target. As the distance from the target increases, the amount of soot and stippling decreases.

A cardboard target backing is covered by a plain white piece of paper. The shooter is positioned so that the muzzle is the desired distance from the paper target. Gripping the pistol with a two-handed grip, the shooter holds the pistol as perfectly vertical as possible. A vertical position is necessary to insure that the soot and stippling are equally distributed and not biased to one side of the point of impact. Each shot is placed onto a different piece of paper so that the stoop and stippling patterns at each distance are isolated from each other.

For this test, the first discharge was with the muzzle flush to the paper target. Discharges were continued at 1 yard increments until the soot and stippling disappeared. Targets were collected from discharges with muzzles at flush to the target, 1 yards, 2 yards, and at 3 yards.

Discharge Test Results

The soot pattern for the discharge with the muzzle flush to the paper target appears below.

Figure 32: Soot Pattern, Muzzle Flush To Target

Significant tearing appears when the muzzle is flush to the paper. This tearing is the result of the muzzle blast ripping the paper with great force.

All of the black areas are the soot (burnt powder) that is deposited by the discharge. Stippling is completely absent in this target. Stippling -- unburned powder -- is blown out the back of the target, along with the muzzle blast.

A very different soot pattern emerges at 1 yard (3 feet).

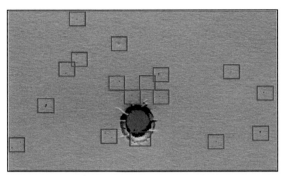

Figure 33: Soot Pattern, Muzzle At 1 Yard From Target

Almost all of the tearing from the muzzle blast has disappeared. A lighter ring of soot surrounds the bullet hole. Soot is spread all around the target zone. Small red boxes are used to identify the soot created by the discharge. Stippling has disappeared completely. Generally, stippling disappears within 36 inches, regardless of caliber. Stippling, heavier unburned powder, loses momentum quickly, falling away from the flight path of the soot.

Moving on to the discharge at 2 yards (6 feet), the following soot pattern is observed:

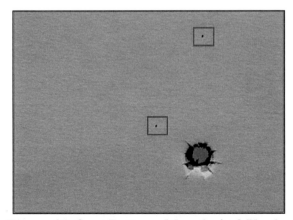

Figure 34: Soot Pattern, Muzzle At 2 Yards

Almost all of the soot has disappeared. Again, a red square is used to identify the locations of the small amount of soot observed at this distance.

After moving the shooter to a position where the muzzle is 3 yards (9 feet), the following soot pattern is observed:

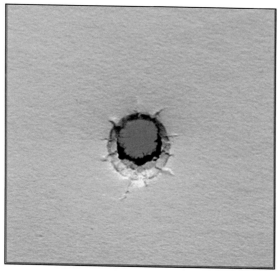

Figure 35: Soot Pattern, Muzzle At 3 Yards

All of the soot and all of the stippling has disappeared at this distance. The dark black inside the bullet hole is actually a shadow artifact, not soot or stippling.

Based on the distance test, a reasonable conclusion is that almost all of the soot and all of the stippling has disappeared when the muzzle is about 8' from the target.

Wilson was at least 8' from Brown with every discharge of the pistol.

Summary and Conclusions

Important elements to remember from this section include the following:

The heaver bullet was selected for this test to provide the maximum shooting distance at which soot and stippling would disappear.

As the distance from the target increases, the amount of soot and stippling decreases.

With Wilson's pistol and similar ammunition, almost all of the soot and all of the stippling has disappeared when the muzzle is about 8' from the target.

Wilson was at least 8' from Brown with every discharge of the pistol.

Reconstructing Wound Bullet Paths

If enough information is provided by the Medical Examiner/Coroner in the Autopsy Report, a bullet path through the body is easily reconstructed on another person.

This author has developed a device that enables this reconstruction. In this section, the device is described. device usage to represent bullet paths at various angles is then demonstrated. Usage of the device as applied to the Wilson/Brown incident is covered in a later section.

A Device For Reconstructing Wound Bullet Paths

A device tool must satisfy a number of requirements.

Entrance and exit wounds, if any, of a bullet path through the body may appear anywhere on the body. So, a reconstruction device must be capable of being located anywhere on the body.

Ultimately, a wound bullet path is also characterized by an impact angle and/or exit angle. These angles may be determined implicitly by the combined entrance and exit wounds or explicitly provided in the Autopsy Report.

Therefore, any device that reconstructs wound bullet path must be capable of being placed anywhere on the body and capable of representing the impact and/or exit angles. Since the human body is a very complex shape, the device must accommodate a wide variety of shapes and body positions.

Components of such a device are shown below.

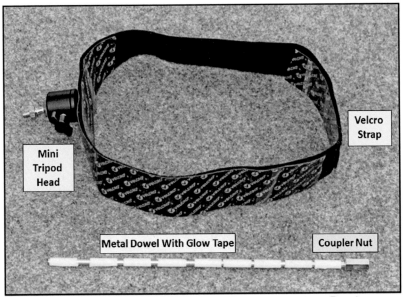

Figure 36: Body Wound Path Reconstruction Device

Accommodation of varying body locations is accomplished by the velcro strap that forms the base of the device. This strap can fit around the head, horizontally or vertically, or around any body part angle in any way and of any width. The strap is locked in place by the velcro portion at the end of the strap.

A mini video tripod head is secured and fixed to the strap using a nut, washers of various sizes, and a bolt. This video head rotates 180° in all directions and possesses a locking mechanism that locks the video heard firmly the desired position. With the device strapped into place on the body and the video head rotated and locked in position, the impact and/or exit angle of the bullet is faithfully accurately represented.

The combined strap and video head enable accurate representation of the entrance and/or exit wounds. Replicating the impact or exit

136

portions of the bullet path involves a few extra parts. A dowel is used to provide the flat, straight external portion of either the entrance bullet path or the exit bullet path . Glow tape is wrapped around the dowel, so that the dowel stands out in photographs. A coupler nut is utilized to connect the dowel to the mini video head.

Capturing the entrance and/or exit angles involves several steps. Place the device in the location of the entrance or exit location. Tighten the strap to hold the device in place. Attach the dowel to the mini video head using the coupler nut. Orient the dowel to the desired angle. Tighten the locking mechanism of the mini video head. Repeat these steps for both the entrance wound and the exit wound, if any.

A protractor is used to position the mini video head and the dowel. Some adjustment may be necessary to the entrance and exit path dowels to insure that the dowels properly align from a side view of the body. After making these fine-tuning adjustments, the entrance and/or exit angles need to be checked to insure that the angles are maintained.

Using The Reconstructing Device

Some simple examples demonstrate the flexibility of the mini video head component of the device in representing entrance angles.

A few figures follow that demonstrate the use of the device to visualize a series of entrance wounds to the head. The device is wrapped around the head of the actor.

If the wound enters through the **top** of the head with a bullet path vertically downward through the head, then the device is wrapped vertically around the head.

Figure 37: Vertical Entrance Wound

All of the other examples represent a bullet wound to the **forehead**. In these wounds, the device is placed horizontally across the head. The dowel is adjusted according to the entrance wound impact angle

Figure 38: Horizontal Entrance Wound

Figure 39: Downward Angled Entrance Wound

Figure 40: Upward Angled Entrance Wound

One bullet path through Brown's body was almost vertical through the top of the head. The other bullet path was downward angled through the forehead. Two of the bullet paths in the figures above demonstrate that this device possesses the visual capability to represent the bullet paths in the Brown case.

Using the mini video head, a wound path at any combination of angles relative to the various body planes can be constructed on another person.

Figure 41: Entrance Wound with Vertical, Horizontal Angles

All of the examples in the previous figure used a single angle, either in the horizontal or the vertical plane. This figure demonstrates that the device is easily used to represent a combination of angles. A downward angle bullet path in the vertical plane and a right angle bullet path in the horizontal plane are displayed in this figure. The bullet path represented by the dowel is downward and from left to right, relative to the body of the victim. Entrance and/or exit angles are always interpreted relative to the body of the victim, not the body of the viewer.

Comparison With Other Cases

While the device developed by the author is the most effective, other possible approaches do exist for replicating the bullet path through the body.

Other approaches need to meet the same criteria satisfied by the author developed reconstruction device. The approach used must be capable of being placed anywhere on the body and capable of representing the entrance and/or exit angles.

In one case, the body was found lying face down on the ground. Based on the Investigation Report, the shooter was leaning over the victim lying on the ground. A Coroner's Report described the wound path by an entrance location and an impact angle.

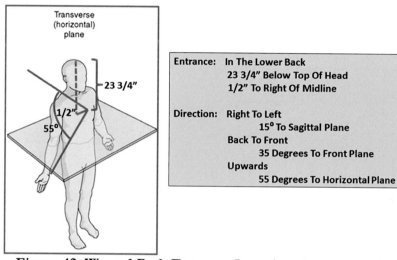

Figure 42: Wound Path Entrance Location, Impact Angle

According to the Coroner in the case, the bullet entered the body in the lower back and 23 3/4" below the top of the head and 1/2" to the right of the midline. Impact angle was 55° relative to the horizontal plane and 15° right to left along the sagittal plane (left to right plane of the body).

For this reconstruction, a tripod was used to stabilize the wound path dowel. A protractor was employed to actually measure the impact angles in the multiple planes for the dowel setup.

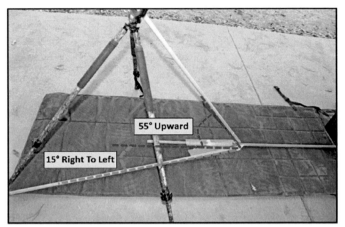

Figure 43: Tripod Usage to Establish Bullet Path

This setup required two dowels to represent the impact angles: one for the horizontal angle (up/down) supported by the tripod, another for the left to right angle. The tripod is positioned so that the downward angled dowel is above the right to left dowel.

Using the tripod and the downward angled dowel, an actor is positioned to demonstrate the most likely position of the shooter.

Figure 44: Using Tripod, Dowels to Position Shooter

Another possible position is that the shooter could be leaning close in to the shooter, along the same downward angled dowel.

Figure 45: Alternate Shooter Position Using Tripod, Dowels

However, the Coroner's report indicated that the wound did not exhibit any soot or stippling, so the close in shooting position does not make sense. Otherwise, the wound would have exhibited soot and stippling.

Summary and Conclusions

A summary of the key points from this section include the following:

- Any device that reconstructs wound bullet path must be capable of being placed anywhere on the body and capable of representing the entrance and/or exit angles.

- A device that meets these requirements uses a velcro strap to place the device anywhere on the body.

- This device uses a mini video head that enables accurate representation of the entrance and/or exit wound path.

- Simple examples demonstrate that this device can accurately represent the primary wound paths in Brown's body.

- Entrance and/or exit angles are always interpreted relative to the body of the victim, not the body of the viewer.

Evaluating Alternate Theories Using Visualization

A systematic approach combines multiple sources of science, experimental data, and actual evidence to evaluate theories of the incident. In this section, the following sources:

- Wilson was 1" shorter than Brown **(actual evidence)**,
- the bullet paths through the body **(actual evidence)**,
- the flat and straight bullet trajectory through the air **(science)**,
- the soot and stippling distance results **(experimental data)**

are **combined** with each theory of the incident (victim body position) to evaluate each specific theory from the Incident Report **(actual evidence)**.

Each theory of the incident involves a body position of the victim, a body position of the shooter, a specific trajectory bullet path through the air, and a specific wound path through the body. A tripod and rods are used to represent the trajectory bullet path. Using the wound path reconstruction device, the bullet path through the body is represented.

Once victim body, shooter body, wound path and trajectory path are reconstructed for the theory of the incident, several criteria are used to evaluate the theory. **A scientifically possible theory of the incident must satisfy the following criteria**:

- trajectory path of the bullet through the air must align with the wound path of the bullet through the body given the specific body position of the victim; and,

- position of the hand of shooter must enable an accurate shot to be accomplished.

For the trajectory path of the bullet through the air to align with the wound path through the body, the angle between the trajectory path and the wound path must be 0°. Any difference between the trajectory path and the wound path indicates that the alternate theory under analysis is not scientifically possible.

A normal hand position for placing an accurate hit requires that the eyes, the pistol sights, and the impact location lie along a single line that connects all three elements. Any shooter position that results in the shooting hand above or below the line of sight between the shooter and the point of impact on the victim also indicates that the body position is not a valid position for the shooter.

Five possible alternate theories of the incident were derived from the Incident Report. These theories were as follows:

- Brown standing/surrendering
- Brown standing/surrendering/head bowed
- Brown charging
- Brown on his knees
- Brown flat on the ground.

Results from the soot and stippling distance test show that Wilson was at least 8' from Brown at the time of all shots.

Bullet path descriptions from the Medical Examiner's Report provide the almost vertical bullet wound paths through the body as well as one chest path through the body.

Selecting The Actors

Two actors were used for the visual reconstructions, one for Wilson, one for Brown.

Figure 46: Actors Representing Wilson and Brown

These actors are not the same weight or the same height as Wilson and Brown. However, for purposes of comparing bullets paths, their height difference is perfect.

Wilson is 1" shorter than Brown. The actor representing Wilson is 1" shorter than the actor representing Brown. This relative height difference is the key to comparing bullet paths under the various theories of the incident. Regardless of the actual heights of the participants, since the height difference is the same, the relative bullet paths and entrance angles are also the same.

Significant weight difference between Wilson and Brown is considered later.

Representing The Head Shots To Brown

Wound path 1, initiated by wound 1, was the bullet that ended the life of Brown. Using the bullet path device, this wound path is shown on the actor representing Brown.

Figure 47: Actor With Device Showing Wound Path 1

The entry wound is 7.87" above the level of the right auditory meatus and at the midline of the vertex of the head. In simple terms, the bullet path entry is approximately at the crest of the head. Path direction is downward and towards the right side of the body. Resting place of the bullet is in the soft tissue on the right side of the face.

Imagine a line moving upward vertically from the hole in the right ear. When this line reaches the level of the top of the head, then come across to the center of the head. That location is where the mini video head of the device is position. Now, look that dowel/rod with the glow tape. The dowel has been positioned to be angled downward and rightward (toward the right side of the body).

This location setup of the device on the head of the actor playing Brown correctly and accurately represents this first bullet path through the body of Brown.

Now, imagine extending the dowel through the head towards the right cheek, where the bullet finally came to rest. This bullet clearly passes through the brain. Any bullet passing through the brain is probably going to cause death, most of the time

A second wound path is caused by wounds 2 and 3.

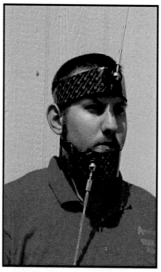

Figure 48: Actor With Devices Showing Wound Path 2

This path is continued through the chest with wound 4. Both entry and exit paths are represented using two copies of the device.

The entry wound is 2.76" above the level of the right auditory meatus and 0.79" right of anterior midline of head. In simple terms, the bullet path entry is somewhere around the center of the forehead. Path direction is downward, backwards, and rearward. The exit of this portion of the bullet path is out of the right jaw.

Using the entry description above, from the Medical Examiner's Report, the entry path dowel is oriented as described. After the entry dowel has been adjusted, the exit dowel is adjusted to match the angle of the entry dowel, when viewed from the side of the actor.

This entry wound was traced around the head earlier, so a repeated explanation should be unnecessary.

Imagine the bullet path through the head that connects the entry dowel and the exit dowel. This angled path bypasses the brain and mostly destroys tissue and bone, just as described by the Medical Examiner's Report.

Representing A Relatively Straight, Flat Trajectory Path

A relatively straight, flat trajectory bullet path over a short distance through the air is easily represented.

Figure 49 Representing Trajectory Paths Using PVC Pipe

Two distances are used in the reconstruction. Minimum soot and stippling distance was found to be 8'. By using a connector, two sections of 4' PVC pipe, 1/2" in diameter, are constructed to represent the 8' bullet paths. In the next section, a comparative analysis of the alternate theories of the incident is accomplished at 4' shooting distance. A single PVC pipe, 1/2" in diameter is used to represent this shorter distance. Bright tape is placed at regular intervals on all of the pipes to enable the trajectories to stand out from the background.

Placing the pipes in the air is accomplished using tripods.

Figure 50: Using Tripods To Represent Trajectory Path

Since the trajectory path of the bullet is through the air, a pair of tripods is used as a mounting setup for the PVC pipe that represents the actual bullet path. Since the tripods possess collapsible legs, a bullet path can be displayed at any height or at up/down or sideways angle.

A specific height for the bullet path through the air can be achieved by some combination of spreading the legs outward or collapsing the legs to a lower height.

Visualizing a Specific Alternate Theory of the Incident

Visualization of a specific alternate theory involves an actor for the shooter, an actor for the victim, the wound path reconstruction device, the bullet path reconstruction device (PVC pipes and tripods), and a pistol.

Steps to establish the visualization are as follows:

- locate the entry wound on the outside of the body of the victim
- if the wound path possesses a bullet resting place, locate the nearest location to the bullet resting place on the outside of the body of the victim
- if the wound path possesses an exit wound, locate the exit wound on the body of the victim
- place a wound reconstruction device with a rotating head over the marked location of the entrance wound
- place another wound reconstruction device with a rotating head over the marked location of the resting place or the exit wound
- align the two dowels for entrance and exit/resting place devices so that the dowels represent a straight line through the body
- place the victim body in the position indicated by the alternate theory of the incident

- establish the trajectory bullet path through the air to the entrance wound location using the PVC pipes and the tripods

- place the shooter body at the opposite end of the trajectory bullet path through the air from the victim body

- place the shooter hand holding a pistol at the start of the trajectory bullet path

- photograph the whole visualization including shooter, victim, bullet path through the air, and wound path through the body

- measure the angular difference between the trajectory bullet path and the wound bullet path

- note the location of the pistol hand relative to the accurate shooting position.

This step by step procedure insures that the relationship among shooter, pistol, trajectory path, victim position, and wound path are all faithfully represented in the visualization.

Given that the relationship among these elements is accurately represented, the criteria for evaluating the alternate theory are also accurate. If the trajectory bullet path and the wound bullet path coincide and if the pistol position properly aligned for accuracy, then the alternate theory **IS** scientifically possible.

If either the trajectory bullet path and the wound bullet path do not coincide or if the pistol position properly aligned for accuracy or both, then the alternate theory **IS NOT** scientifically possible.

Evaluating The Alternate Theories With The Head Shot

Since the soot and stippling distance testing determines that the minimum shooting distance is 8', all the alternate theories are initially evaluated at a distance of 8'.

Wound path 1 (wound 1) was the, with entrance wound through the top of the head, is the basis for these reconstructions.

Pistol hand position in each scenario is placed in such a way as to minimize the angle between the trajectory bullet path through the air and the wound bullet path through the body. **The purpose in taking this approach initially is to position the trajectory path as close as is physically possible to the wound path.** This position is then compared with the line of sight that would enable the shooter to accomplish an accurate shot placement to the entry wound without necessarily matching the wound path.

The first alternate theory of the incident is Brown standing/surrendering with Wilson standing 8' from Brown.

Figure 51: Brown Standing/Surrendering At 8'

In this theory of the incident, body position of Brown is standing/surrendering. The green colored dowel in the head of the actor representing Brown is wound path 1. Trajectory bullet path through the air is 90° from the wound bullet path through the body under these conditions. This angle shows that in this theory of the incident, the trajectory path significantly differs from the wound path.

Line of sight is the line between the eyes of the shooter and the point of impact. In order to minimize the angle between the trajectory path and the wound path, the actor representing Wilson has to hold the pistol fairly high above the line of sight. Completing an accurate shot into the point of impact in the top of the head is impossible with the pistol located at this position.

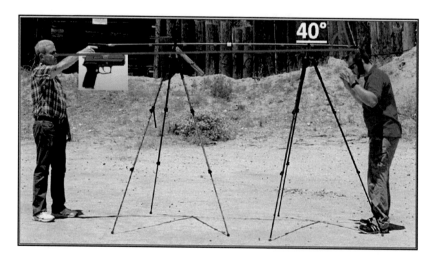

Figure 52: Standing/Surrendering With Line Of Sight

If the pistol were brought down into the line of sight, so that the pistol sights were accessible to the eyes of the shooter, then the trajectory path would align with the line of sight. In this situation, the angle between the trajectory path and the wound path would be even greater than 90°. This greater angle can be seen in the figure above because the red line of sight is below the trajectory path through the air, which is at 90° to the wound path represented by the dowel.

Since the trajectory bullet path and the wound bullet path do not coincide, whether or not the pistol position is properly aligned for accuracy, the alternate theory of **Brown standing/surrendering is not scientifically possible and could not have happened**.

The next alternate theory of the incident is Brown standing/surrendering with his head bowed forward in submission and with Wilson standing 8' from Brown.

A submissive position is one in which the person has the head and shoulders leaning forward.

Figure 53: Brown Surrendering, Head In Submission

156

With the hand raised to the highest possible position, trajectory path and wound path are still 40° apart. So, bowing the head in submission does make a significant difference in the angle between the trajectory path and the wound path. **However, this difference in angle is not enough to enable Wilson to obtain wound path 1, the killing path.**

A trajectory path based on the line of sight of Wilson also does not enable Wilson to obtain a trajectory path that matches the wound path in this body position.

Figure 54: Surrendering, Head Bowed With Line Of Sight

Bringing the pistol down to Brown's line of sight actually increases the angle between the trajectory path and the wound path. This difference in angle is greater than 40°, still far less than the 90° difference is Brown was standing upright.

Since the trajectory bullet path and the wound bullet path do not coincide, whether or not the pistol position is properly aligned for accuracy, the alternate theory of **Brown standing/surrendering**

157

with his head bowed in submission is not scientifically possible and could not have happened.

In this next theory of the incident, Brown is kneeling, again with his head bowed in submission. With Wilson at least the 8' away from Brown, a difference still exists between trajectory path and wound path.

In this body position, the shooting hand position has been modified. In discussing this incident with law enforcement officers who have been in an shooting incident, many officers claimed that a natural response is to fire without aiming. So, a non-aiming pistol position is used in this theory.

Figure 55: Brown Kneeling, Head In Submission

Even with Brown on his knees and the pistol hand in a more natural, non-aiming position, an angular difference exists between the trajectory path through the air and the wound path through the body.

Trajectory path and wound path differ by an angle of 25° when Brown is kneeling in submission and the shooting hand is held in a non-aiming position. This difference in angle between the two paths is still substantial.

Raising the pistol up to the line of sight of Wilson does not result in a trajectory path that matches the wound path.

Figure 56: Kneeling, Head In Submission, Line Of Sight

This adjustment to the shooting hand position reduces the angular difference between the trajectory path, but only slightly. This reduction in angle is not sufficient to enable the trajectory path to match the wound path.

Since the trajectory bullet path and the wound bullet path do not coincide, whether or not the pistol position is non-aimed, the alternate theory of **Brown kneeling with his head bowed in submission is not scientifically possible and could not have happened**.

Some sources reported that Brown was on his knees, that Wilson executed Brown. This theory of the incident could only have occurred if Wilson was up close. If Wilson had been up close and Brown kneeling, Brown would have soot and stippling on those entry wound to this wound path. According to the Medical

Examiner's Report, none of the entry wounds in Brown's body exhibited any soot and stippling. So, this execution theory is just not scientifically possible.

One last theory of the incident remains -- Brown is charging.

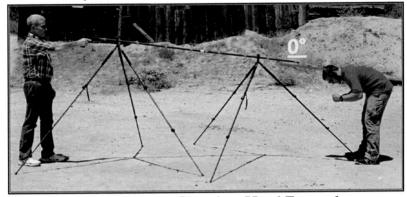

Figure 57: Brown Charging, Head Forward

In this body position, the trajectory path through the air matches the wound path through the body. Trajectory path and wound path exhibit an angular difference of 0°. So, this theory of the incident is scientifically sound, unlike all the other possible theories.

The line of sight and the trajectory path also are in alignment.

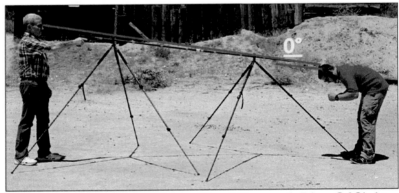

Figure 58: Brown Charging, Head Forward, Line Of Sight

In this body position, the line of sight, the trajectory path, and the wound path are **ALL** in perfect alignment.

Since the line of sight, the trajectory bullet path and the wound bullet path perfectly coincide, the alternate theory of **Brown charging is scientifically correct and is exactly what happened**.

Visual Comparison Summary

A complete reasonable range of alternate theories of the incident have been evaluated.

Brown Position	Degrees, 8'	Hand Position, 8'
Surrender	90	Abnormal
Surrender Submissive	40	Abnormal
Kneeling	25	Abnormal
Charging	0	Normal

Table 11: Visual Comparison Summary

In the first column appears all of the positions of Brown determined as the alternate theories of the incident. Column two (2) provides the angle between the trajectory path and the wound path for each alternate theory. Contained in the last column are the evaluation of the pistol hand when positioned to minimize the angle between the trajectory path and the wound path.

As concluded above, the only position of Brown's body that can be scientifically correct is if Brown is charging. This body position and its evaluation is identified by a surrounding green rectangle.

This summary provides another important insight into the alternate theories of the incident. As Brown's upper body approaches parallel to ground, difference angle between trajectory and wound path approaches 0°. So, position of Brown's upper body is the key indicator as to the position of Brown's body when the wound path was created.

Sequence Of Head Shots

Using the wound path reconstruction device, the sequence of the head shots is easily determined.

Figure 59: Head Shots Using Reconstruction Device

Both head shots are represented using the wound path reconstruction device. The bottom entrance wound in the head occurred first. This wound was received when Brown was charging with his head slightly upward, so he could see where he was charging.

Once the first impact hit Brown, he started to fall forward. As he fell forward, the head started to fall face downward. Then, second entrance wound in the top of the head was created from a different trajectory path.

The entrance wound on top of the head could not have been created first. If this wound had been created first and the body started to fall forward, the top of the forehead would be facing downward. Then, the entrance wound in the top of the forehead simply would not have been received.

Comparison With Other Cases

In many cases, bullet impacts into terminal materials are recorded by the crime scene reconstruction team. These impacts are visually recorded by the insertion of dowels into the impact hole.

Figure 60: Bullet Impact With Dowel

A dowel is chosen that is the approximate diameter of the hole in the terminal material. This dowel, composed of a fairly stiff material, is then inserted into the impact hole. When the dowel is released, gravity positions the dowel in the hole at the same angles as the bullet path through the hole.

These visualizations are often, **BUT NOT ALWAYS**, characterized by an additional set of measurements.

Impact	Distance From Ground	Up/Down Direction	Angle
B	24 ¾"	Unable To Determine	Unable To Determine
C	44"	Downward	50° East -> West
D	28 ¾"	Upward	75° West -> East
E	17 ¼"	Downward	45° North -> South
F	25 ½"	Upward	North -> South
H	28 ¾" (Bottom Of Legs)	Unable To Determine	Unable To Determine

Table 12: Crime Scene Team Bullet Impact Summary

This table is an actual bullet impact summary from a real shooting incident. In general, three measurements are necessary to characterize the impact: height above the ground, up/down angle, left/right angle. These measurements are supposed to be the contents of the above table. Unfortunately, the last column is a bit garbled. However, given the orientation of the room at the location of the incident, East => West turns out to be Left => Right. And, North => South also turns out to be Left => Right.

This table is then used as proof that the accused actually performed the shooting. The problem is that the dowel is nothing more than the end of the trajectory path. In order to determine who, what, when, where, and how, the trajectory path must be reversed.

Two viable methods are available to perform a reverse trajectory.

Figure 61: Methods For Reversing A Trajectory

Every object that moves through the air may be described by two paths: a flight path and a ground path. As long as the ground is fairly level, the ground path predicts the reverse trajectory as accurately as the air path. This statement is especially true for bullet trajectory paths over short distances, out to 50 yards.

A reverse trajectory from a bullet impact is necessary because this path helps to identify the location of the shooter. A lot can be determined by knowing the location of the shooter. For instance, if witnesses state that the accused was at a different location from the location determined by the reverse trajectory, then the accused is innocent.

The impact characterizations are important data to start a shooting reconstruction. But, these characterizations by themselves are nothing but data and do not provide much information about the guilt or innocence of the accused.

Summary and Conclusions

A few important concepts and conclusions identified in this section include the following:

- Each theory of the incident involves a body position of the victim, a body position of the shooter, a specific trajectory bullet path through the air, and a specific wound path through the body.

- For the trajectory path of the bullet through the air to align with the wound path through the body, the angle between the trajectory path and the wound path must be $0°$.

- A normal hand position for placing an accurate hit requires that the eyes, the pistol sights, and the impact location lie along a single line that connects all three.

- If the trajectory bullet path and the wound bullet path coincide and if the pistol position properly aligned for accuracy, then the alternate theory **IS** scientifically possible.

- If either the trajectory bullet path and the wound bullet path do not coincide or if the pistol position properly aligned for accuracy or both, then the alternate theory **IS NOT** scientifically possible.

- Since the trajectory bullet path and the wound bullet path do not coincide, whether or not the pistol position is properly aligned for accuracy, the alternate theory of **Brown standing/surrendering is not scientifically possible and could not have happened**.

166

- Bowing the head in submission does make a significant difference in the angle between the trajectory path and the wound path.

- However, this difference in angle is not enough to enable Wilson to obtain wound path 1, the killing path.

- Since the trajectory bullet path and the wound bullet path do not coincide, whether or not the pistol position is properly aligned for accuracy, the alternate theory of **Brown standing/surrendering with his head bowed in submission is not scientifically possible and could not have happened**.

- Since the trajectory bullet path and the wound bullet path do not coincide, whether or not the pistol position is non-aimed, the alternate theory of **Brown kneeling with his head bowed in submission is not scientifically possible and could not have happened**.

- Since the line of sight, the trajectory bullet path and the wound bullet path perfectly coincide, the alternate theory of **Brown charging is scientifically correct and is exactly what happened**.

- Position of Brown's upper body is the key indicator as to the position of Brown's body when the wound path was created.

  - The entrance wound in the top of the forehead was the first head wound received. As Brown's body fell forward, the head fell forward. Then, the wound in the top of the head occurred.

Evaluating Alternate Theory Uncertainty

All of the previous evaluations were performed at the minimum soot and stippling disappearance distance of 8'. In order to consider possible uncertainty in this distance, each theory of the incident is also evaluated at a shorter distance than the soot and stippling distance.

The goal of using a shorter distance is to see if the evaluation of each alternate theory changes or stays the same with changes in distance.

As a basis for comparison, the shooting distance of 4' is used in this analysis. The same terminal head wound/bullet path 1 forms the basis of these evaluations. This entrance wound/bullet path is represented by the same green colored dowel using the bullet path reconstruction device.

Comparing the difference angles between trajectory path and wound path at both 8' and 4' enables inferences regarding the angular difference at even greater distances.

Analysis of the Head Shot At A Shorter Distance

Four alternate theories are considered at this distance, just as before:

- Brown standing/surrendering
- Brown standing/surrendering with his head bowed
- Brown kneeling with his head bowed
- Brown charging.

The first theory of the incident evaluated is Brown standing/surrendering.

Figure 62: Brown Standing/Surrendering At 4'

Even reaching as high as possible, a 90° difference angle exists between the bullet trajectory path and the wound path in the body.

Brown standing/surrendering is still not scientifically possible at this shorter distance and could not have happened.

Brown surrendering with his head in submission is the next theory of the incident to be evaluated at this distance.

Figure 63: Brown Surrendering, Head Bowed, At 4'

Even reaching as high as possible, a 45° difference angle exists between the bullet trajectory path and the wound path in the body.

<u>**Brown standing/surrendering with his head in submission is still not scientifically possible at this shorter distance and could not have happened**</u>.

Brown kneeling and surrendering is the next position of interest.

Figure 64: Brown Kneeling And Surrendering At 4'

Using the same non-aiming pistol position, a 40° difference angle exists between the bullet trajectory path and the wound path in the body.

<u>Brown kneeling/surrendering with his head in submission is still not scientifically possible at this shorter distance and could not have happened</u>.

Finally, the charging position is evaluated with the Wilson at 4' from Brown.

Figure 65: Brown Charging At 4'

With Brown charging, a 0° difference angle exists between the bullet trajectory path and the wound path in the body.

<u>Brown charging is scientifically possible at this shorter distance and could have happened</u>.

However, at this separation distance between Wilson and Brown, soot and stippling would have appeared at the entrance wound. Since soot and stippling did not appear at the entrance wound, as stated in the Medical Examiner's Report, this theory of the incident did not occur. While scientifically possible from the perspective of the trajectory and wound path angle difference, this theory is scientifically impossible from the perspective of the soot and stippling distance for Wilson's pistol and comparative ammunition.

Visual Comparison Summary

A summary of the results of the visual comparison of the difference angles appears in the table below.

Brown Position	Degrees, 8'	Hand Position, 8'	Degrees, 4'	Hand Position, 4'
Surrender	90	Abnormal	90	Abnormal
Surrender Submissive	40	Abnormal	45	Abnormal
Kneeling	25	Abnormal	40	Abnormal
Charging	0	Normal	0	Abnormal

Table 13: Visual Comparison Summary At 4'

This table compares the difference angles between the trajectory path and the wound path at the distances of both 8' and 4'.

As with the visual reconstructions at 8', the only scientifically possible theory of the incident is with Brown charging. In this body position, no difference angle exists between the bullet trajectory path and the wound path. In all the other body positions, a significant different exists between the bullet trajectory path and the wound path.

However, while scientifically possible based on body position, this theory of the incident did not occur at this distance, due to the lack of soot and stippling on the entrance wound.

This table also reveals the behavior of the difference angle as the distance between Wilson and Brown increases. As the distance moves from 4' to 8', the difference angle between bullet trajectory and wound paths decreases somewhat.

So, if Wilson were greater than 8' from Brown, this difference angle would grow even smaller. However, if the distance between Wilson and Brown had been greater, then the spread of the fired casings would have been different. The spread of fired casings was 22' 8', indicating that Wilson moved 22' 8". As will be shown, this distance of movement and the fired casing location spread is consistent with Wilson shooting at 8' distances from Brown.

Summary And Conclusions

Important conclusions from this evaluation of a 4' separation between Wilson and Brown are as follows:

- Brown charging is the only scientifically possible theory of the incident at this shorter distance and could have happened.

- However, this theory is scientifically impossible from the perspective of the soot and stippling distance for Wilson's pistol and comparative ammunition.

- As the distance moves from 4' to 8', the difference angle between bullet trajectory and wound paths decreases somewhat.

- If the distance between Wilson and Brown had been greater, then the spread of the fired casings would have been different.

Evaluating The Lateral Right Chest Wound Path

Wound path one (1) through the top of the head clearly demonstrates that Brown was charging at the time of impact. If Brown was charging, wound path three (3) entering through the lateral right chest would also be in a downward direction and indicate that the upper body was parallel to the ground. In this section, wound path three (3) is evaluated. The only alternate theories evaluated in this section are with Brown standing and Brown charging.

Representation Of Lateral Right Chest Wound Path

Using the specifications of this wound path from the Medical Examiner's Report, this wound path is reconstructed. Entry location and bullet resting location are indicated by a black marker that sticks to the shirt. The approximate external location associated with the internal bullet resting place is marked for reconstruction purposes.

Figure 66: Locating The Lateral Right Wound Path

Entry point for this wound path is 7.87" below the right auditory meatus and 8.66" to the right of the anterior (front) midline of the chest. This wound path is downward, backward, and to the right with the bullet coming to rest by fracturing the 8th right rib and coming to rest in the soft tissue just past the broken rib.

Using two of the wound path reconstruction devices, the entry location and the resting place of the bullet are located on the body of an actor.

Figure 67: Entry Wound, Bullet Rest Location, Chest Path

At the right, a green circle depicts the location of the entry wound to this wound path. A circle appearing at the left indicates the approximate internal location of the resting place of the bullet. This location is just below the location of the 8th rib, as shown earlier. Once the entry location and the resting place of the bullet have been located, the wound path is easily identified. The wound path through the body follows a straight line between the entry. This straight line appears as a green line connecting the entry wound location and the bullet resting location. If the bullet path was changed by interaction with some bone structure such as the ribs, this path modification would have been indicated in the Medical Examiner's Report.

In order to evaluate the bullet trajectory paths, the wound path angle must be determined relative to the vertical axis of the body.

Figure 68: Measured Angle Of Chest Wound Path

Using a protractor, the angle of the wound path relative to the vertical axis of the body is actually measured. Given this entry location and bullet wound path, the wound path angle is 40° relative to the vertical axis of the body.

Evaluating Chest Wound Path With Brown Standing

Using the PVC pipes and the tripods, a trajectory bullet path is constructed with Wilson discharging at 8' distance and with Brown standing.

Figure 69: Chest Wound, Trajectory Paths, Brown Standing

After constructing the bullet trajectory path with Wilson at 8' distance, the angle of the bullet trajectory path is measured relative to the vertical axis of the body. This angle is determined to be 90°.

In order for this wound path to confirm the theory of the incident with Brown standing, the bullet trajectory path angle must match the wound path angle. These angles are both determined relative to the vertical axis of the body.

Comparing the reconstructed trajectory path angle with the wound path angle allows evaluation of this position with Brown standing.

Figure 70: Wound, Trajectory Path Angles, Standing

The bullet trajectory path angle is shown in red and is measured to be 90°. In comparison, the wound path angle is depicted in green and is measured to be 40°.

Since the wound path angle and the bullet trajectory path angle do not match, Brown could not have been standing during the time at which the wound path was created.

Given the difference between these two angles, relative to the vertical axis of Brown's body, the theory of the incident with Brown standing/surrendering is not corroborated. This theory of the incident is still not scientifically possible.

Evaluating Chest Wound Path With Brown Charging

Using the same approach, the chest and trajectory wound paths are evaluated under the theory of the incident that has Brown charging, rather than standing/surrendering.

Figure 71: Chest Wound, Trajectory Paths, Brown Charging

After constructing the bullet trajectory path with Wilson at 8' distance, the angle of the bullet trajectory path is measured relative to the vertical axis of the body. This angle is determined to be 40°.

Comparison of the trajectory and wound path angles relative to the vertical axis of the body appears below.

Figure 72: Wound, Trajectory Path Angles, Charging

The bullet trajectory path angle is shown in red and is measured to be r0°. In comparison, the wound path angle is depicted in green and is also measured to be 40°.

Since the wound path angle and the bullet trajectory path angle do match, Brown was charging during the time at which the wound path was created.

Given that these two angles are the same, relative to the vertical axis of Brown's body, the theory of the incident with Brown charging is corroborated. This corroboration of this theory of the incident further demonstrates that this theory scientifically possible.

Comparison Of The Head, Chest Wound Path Methods

The approach used to evaluate the chest wound path differs somewhat from the approach used in evaluating the head path.

In the head path evaluation, the angular difference between the head wound path and the trajectory wound path was directly measured.

In this chest wound path evaluation, both the angle of the bullet trajectory path and the bullet wound path were measured relative to the vertical axis of the body. The vertical axis of the body serves as a common reference for both angle measurements.

Either approach is valid and gives the same result. This analysis used this second approach simply to demonstrate that multiple approaches can be used.

Summary And Conclusions

Key points from this chapter include the following:

- wound path angle through the lateral right chest is 40^0 relative to the vertical axis of the body.

- trajectory path angle with Brown standing is 90^0 relative to the vertical axis of the body.

- since the chest wound path angle and the bullet trajectory path angle do not match, Brown could not have been standing during the time at which the chest wound path was created.

- wound path angle with Brown charging is 40^0 relative to the vertical axis of the body.

- since the wound path angle and the bullet trajectory path angle do match, Brown was charging during the time at which the chest wound path was created.

Fired Casing Area and Ejection Pattern Overlay

A systematic approach combines multiple sources of science, experimental data, and actual evidence to evaluate theories of the incident. In this section, the following sources:

- physical location of the fired casings **(actual evidence)**,
- first blood and final body locations **(actual evidence)**,
- the flat and straight bullet trajectory through the air **(science)**,
- combined trajectory, ejection pattern**(systematic integration)**,
- the soot and stippling distance results **(experimental data)**
- ejection pattern of Officer Wilson's pistol **(experimental data)**

are **combined** to determine a series of shooter positions for Officer Wilson. These shooters positions then lead to a clearer understanding of the actions taken by Officer Wilson.

Combining these elements utilizes the core scientific basis for the systematic approach: bullet path/trajectory, shooter location, and ejection direction/ejection angle. These combined elements are compared to the actual fired casing area to identify the ejection pattern areas within the fired casing area.

Ejection pattern overlay is the process of dividing the combined area of the fired casing locations into one or more ejection pattern areas using the experimentally derived ejection pattern. This combination is performed at the actual scale so that the exact locations of the ejection patterns can be determined.

Once the ejection areas are identified, these areas can be used to identify the locations of the shooter. Shooter location is determined using ejection direction/angle, ejection distance, ejection width, straight, flat bullet trajectory, and soot and stippling distance results.

Bounding the Fired Casing Locations

Reviewing the fired casing locations provides clear identification of the total area bounded by the fired casings.

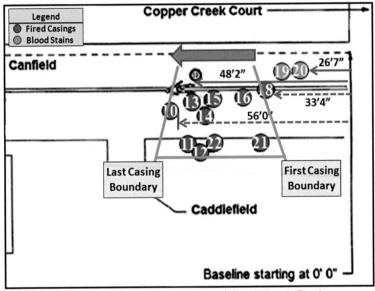

Figure 73: Area Bounded By The Fired Casings

The fired casing area is the area that contains all of the fired casings from Officer Wilson's pistol. In the figure, the fired casing area is outlined by green boundary lines and the centerline of the road.

On the west side of the incident location, the fired casing area is bounded by Item 10, the westernmost fired casing. Item 18 determines the easternmost boundary of the fired casing area. A number of fired casings appear up on the southern sidewalk, slightly past the curb. These casings form the southernmost boundary of the fired casing area. The line between the first blood drop, Item 20, and the final, face down location of the body forms the northern boundary of the fired casing area.

This analysis reveals an important aspect of the fired casing area. Item 18 is 33' 4" from the common reference location. Item 10 is 56' 0". So, the fired casing area is at least 23' across from east to west, measured from the difference in the two fired casing locations. Since Items 18 and 10 are in the middle of the upper and lower boundaries, the distance at the base of the area is greater.

Experimental analysis shows the ejection pattern area for the Sig Sauer P-229 with equivalent ammunition is 8' wide and 13' height at the centerline of the ejection pattern area.

At least three (3) ejection pattern areas that are 8' wide exist within a fired casing area that is at least 23' across from east to west.

Identifying Locations of Fired Casing Area To Scale

A scaled rendering of the fired casing area is the basis for the process of overlaying ejection pattern areas. Google Earth was used to generate the scaled rendering.

Measurement locations were taken from the Grand Jury evidence, as described previously. All measurements shown on the diagram are scaled according to Google Earth.

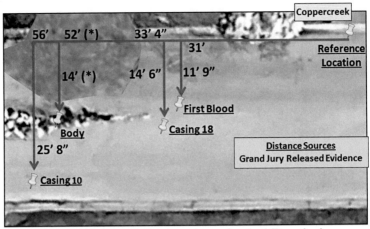

Figure 74: Fired Casing Area Scaled Rendering

Finding a location is simple. All locations in the Grand Jury Evidence Location Map are presented westward and southward from the reference location.

The reference location appears at the upper right corner of the figure. Using the Google Ruler tool, move westward the indicated distance. Mark that location. From the marked location, move southward, again using the Google Ruler Tool. Then, mark the final location.

For instance, the first blood was found 31' westward and 11' 9" southward from the referenced location. These offsets are clearly marked in the figure above. The final location is also marked and labeled.

Google imagery is accurately scaled. Google Ruler Tool uses this scale to determine the actual distance. Therefore, markers shown above are at the actual distances to the physical evidence locations.

These four physical evidence locations along with the southern curb of the road from the boundaries of the fired casing area.

Once the evidence items that form the boundary are located, the physical boundaries of the fired casing area can be highlighted.

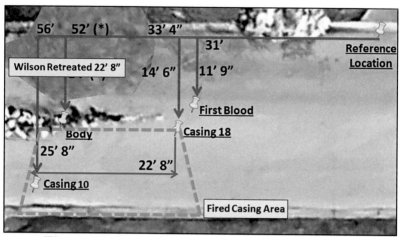

Figure 75: Actual Fired Casing Area Boundaries

A green dashed trapezoid overlay clearly identifies the location of the fired casing area. This boundary area is determined by the indicators described above.

Physical distance between casing 18, the westernmost boundary, and casing 10, the easternmost boundary is 22' 8" This measurement is consistent with earlier conclusion that Wilson retreated 22' 8".

189

Ejection Pattern Overlay Scientific Process

A specific process is used to overlay the ejection patterns onto the fired casing area. In order to perform this overlay, several important items are necessary. The first item is the boundaries of the fired casing area. Additionally, the ejection area dimensions and ejection angle are needed. Finally, a shooting distance is needed. In this case, all of the items are available.

The overlay process consists of very specific steps. These steps are as follows:

- place the ejection areas onto the fired casing area so that the bases of the areas completely cover the widest boundary of the fired casing area and so that none of the areas overlap each other

- for each ejection area,

  ➤ identify the ejection centerline of each ejection area

  ➤ draw the trajectory line at the ejection angle from the apex of the centerline

  ➤ mark the shooting distance along the trajectory line

All of the overlay placement must be performed to scale, just as the fired casing area boundary identification is performed to scale.

This overlay process actually has a mathematical foundation, called convolution. Convolution is the combination of two functions. In this situation, one function is the fired casing area which maps fired casings to physical locations on the ground. A second function relates fired casings into an ejection pattern. The mathematical convolution of these two functions yields a mapping of the ejection pattern onto the fired casing area. Since both functions have fired casing locations as the independent variable, this mathematical combination can be accomplished. Thus, the resultant convolution function relates ejection pattern to fired casing area, without reference to the fired casing locations.

In this case, some very important constraints must be satisfied. The first ejection pattern area must include the first, easternmost casing, casing 18. Moreover, the first trajectory line and shooting distance should match with the location of the first blood. Similar constraints exist for the last ejection pattern area. This ejection pattern area must include the last, westernmost casing, casing 10. Additionally, the last trajectory line and shooting distance should match with the location of Brown's body on the ground.

Ejection pattern overlays must be 8' at the base by 13' along the centerline. Trajectory lines must preserve the 125^0 ejection angle from the ejection pattern centerline. The number of 8' bases must cover the 23' distance along the southernmost, widest boundary of the fired casing area.

Shooter locations must be at a left to right angle from the path of Brown. This requirement stems from the fact that all of the bullet paths were towards the right side of Brown's body. Based on the soot/stippling distance tests, the shooter should be 8' from the known impact locations -- first blood and the center position of the body.

The fired casing area is at least 23' across from east to west along the widest boundary. Multiple ejection pattern areas that are 8' at the base exist within a fired casing area that is at least 23' across from east to west.

Ejection Pattern Overlay Visualization

Using the process outlined above, multiple ejection patterns are placed onto the scaled representation of the fired casing area. These patterns proceed from eastward to westward, are based on the scaled dimensions, and do not overlap.

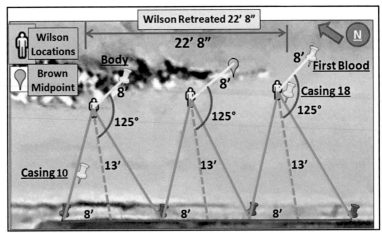

Figure 76: Ejection Patterns Overlaid Onto Fired Casing Area

Each ejection pattern base is identified as a red line. Ejection pattern boundaries appear as green lines. A yellow line is used to represent the trajectory line. Red angle indicators show the ejection angles being applied to the ejection pattern centerline to obtain the trajectory line.

All of the angles and measurements are accurately determined to scale using the Ruler Tool of Google Earth. Ejection patterns

192

visually look to be different sizes. However, this distortion is introduced as a result of rotating the image so that the bottom of the fired casing is parallel to the bottom of the image. Despite this visual distortion, all of the angles and measurements are accurately determined to scale using the Ruler Tool of Google Earth.

Not surprisingly, the 23' base of the fired casing area nicely divides into three (3) ejection patterns when each ejection area base is 8' in width. None of these ejection pattern overlays overlap each other so that the entire fired casing area is well covered.

OK, these overlays may be off by a foot or so. An error of 1' appears when compared to widest 23' boundary of the fired casing area. This error is within a reasonable margin of error for this type of post event analysis. The final conclusions are not affected by this minor and reasonable error.

All of the constraints are satisfied in these overlays of ejection pattern areas. First, easternmost casing 18 is included in the first ejection pattern area. Last, westernmost casing 10 is included in the last ejection pattern area. Shooting positions, trajectory lines, and target locations (first blood, final body position) all align when the ejection pattern overlays are placed.

After moving along the trajectory line of the first and last trajectory by the soot/stippling shooting distance of 8', specifically identified target locations were found. Shooter locations are identified at the apex of each ejection pattern overlay.

At 8' from the shooter location along the trajectory line in the first ejection pattern is found the first blood identified in the Physical Evidence listing. Distance between the shooter location of the last ejection pattern and the location of Brown's body is also 8', the soot/stippling distance.

Finding first blood and the center of Brown's body at the soot/stippling distance along the trajectory line confirms that these ejection patterns are properly placed in the fired casing area.

Given that the accurate placement of the ejection patterns is confirmed, the intermediate location of Brown can be placed onto the overlay diagram. This location is represented by an aqua bubble at 8' from the shooter location and midway between the location of the first blood and the final location of Brown's body.

This set of ejection pattern area overlays actually represents a minimum number of ejection patterns. Unless Wilson moved, then paused at the intermediate and final shooting positions to discharge his firearm, other patterns actually exist within the fired casing area. However, this minimum number of ejection pattern areas enables a specific conclusion about the movement and actions of Wilson.

Wilson was moving backwards while Brown was charging forward. As Wilson retreated, he continually discharged his firearm in an attempt to stop Brown's attack. This movement is explained by the multiple ejection pattern areas inside the fired casing area and by the multiple shooting positions.

Wilson, Brown Direction Of Movement During Incident

Using the physical target locations (first blood, Brown's body) and the shooting positions identified by the ejection pattern overlays, the direction of travel of both participants can be identified.

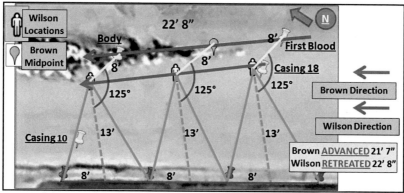

Figure 77: Wilson And Brown Direction Of Movement

A red line represents the direction of movement of Brown. This line is constructed by joining the location of the first blood, the midpoint location and the location of the body.

Using a blue line, the direction of movement of Wilson is identified. Creation of this line is accomplished by linking the multiple shooter locations at the apex of the ejection pattern areas.

From these lines, several conclusions can be identified. Brown advanced 21' 7" while simultaneously Wilson retreated 22' 8". In other words, both participants moved approximately the same distance. Brown's movement of 21' 7' while Wilson discharge 12 cartridges indicates that Brown was moving quickly, not casually walking forward and surrendering.

Informal tests show that a shooter can discharge 12 cartridges while moving backwards over a distance of 22' 8" in 5 - 8 seconds. These numbers translate into a speed of 3 feet / second, assuming the more conservative time estimate of 8 seconds.

Alternative Theories Of Movement By Brown, Wilson

Several other explanations of the movement by the parties have been proposed by witnesses. One explanation is that Wilson was advancing towards Brown discharging rounds while Brown was charging. Another explanation is that Brown was kneeling with Wilson standing over Brown, executing Brown. Neither of these possibilities are supported by the physical evidence.

A scaled graphical representation of the simultaneous charging theory appears in the figure below.

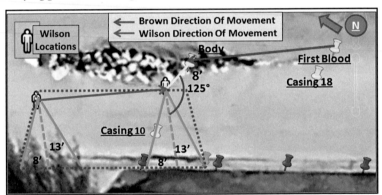

Figure 78: Wilson Advancing, Brown Charging

A red arrow is used to depict the movement of Brown from the first blood location where Brown turned to the final position of the body. Wilson's movement is shown using a blue arrow. Physical locations of actual evidence are replicated for evaluation purposes, including first blood, dead body, easternmost casing (18) and westernmost casing (10). **THESE LOCATIONS ARE FIXED,**

SO ANY REPRESENTATION MUST BE CONSISTENT WITH THESE LOCATIONS OR IS NOT SCIENTIFICALLY POSSIBLE. Blue push pins represent the southernmost boundary of the fired casing locations for comparison purposes.

A new starting position to the westward, is shown for Wilson, farther This starting position is necessary because the final resting location of Brown's body is fixed. In order for Wilson's last discharge to cause the death of Brown at this fixed location, Wilson would have to start further westward.

This new starting location is based upon simple laws of physics. Two objects in uniform motion moving towards each other at different speeds meet somewhere in the middle. Introductory physics classes ask students to calculate the distance to the meeting location using Newton's laws relating distance, speed, and time. Obviously, the starting locations of each object has to be positioned so that the objects meet at the location in the middle predicted by the laws of physics.

A smaller fired casing spread occurs because both Brown and Wilson are moving towards each other so that Wilson would have discharged the cartridges over a shorter distance. A shorter distance results because both Brown and Wilson are moving and meet somewhere in the middle. Thus, Wilson would not have covered any of the distance between the start location of Brown (at the blood spots) and his own start location.

In the figure, a smaller, fired casing area is depicted assuming the new starting location for Wilson. This fired casing area is represented by a quadrangle using a dashed red boundary line.

This fired casing area is a result of the other evidence property locations that are fixed. Soot and stippling distance is 8'. Given this distance and the location of fired casing 18, the location of the easternmost ejection pattern is fixed in the new fired casing area. An ejection pattern fairly near the starting location of Wilson must also be included in the fired casing area.

This new fired casing area, under this theory of movement, is too far to the westward of the actual fired casing area. The easternmost fired casing (18) and, indeed, a large percentage of the fired casings at the scene simply do not fit into this new fired casing area. A large number of actual fired casings, represented by the blue push pins, clearly do not fit within the smaller and more westward fired casing area.

Moreover, given the new starting location for Wilson, far more fired casings should have been found to the westward. However, no fired casings were found to the westward of fired casing 10.

Finally, this fired casing area and implied shooting positions for Wilson simply do not explain the location of the first blood. First blood was dropped after Brown started charging. A bullet impact that caused this blood dropping had to be from the first shooting position. Under the circumstances of fear, stress, and tension, an impact from near the new starting location is not particularly likely.

If Wilson were standing over or near Brown discharging his firearm while Brown was on his knees, the fired casing spread would have been completely different, as shown below.

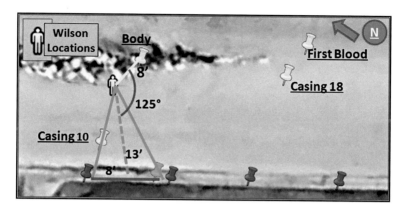

Figure 79: Wilson Standing Over Brown, Brown Kneeling

In this theory, Wilson is actually standing still. Therefore, only one (1) ejection pattern area would appear. All of the fired casings would exist in a triangular area approximately 8' at the base and 13' high at the centerline.

A large percentage of the actual fired casings would not reside within this fired casing area composed of a single ejection pattern area. Fired casing (18) and all of the fired casings around the blue push pins are outside of the boundaries of the single ejection pattern area that represents the fired casing area in this theory.

Furthermore, the cause of the blood at the first blood location is not explained. Under the conditions which Wilson faced, the likelihood of an impact from Wilson's shooting position is questionable.

Fired casings areas that would be created under these alternate theories of movement do not incorporate all of the locations of the actual physical evidence. Therefore, these theories of movement are not scientifically possible.

199

Summary and Conclusions

Important points identified in this chapter include the following:

- ejection pattern overlay is the process of dividing the combined area of the fired casing locations into one or more ejection areas using the experimentally derived ejection pattern.

- fired casing area is the area that contains all of the fired casings from Officer Wilson's pistol.

- fired casing area in this situation is at least 23' across from east to west along the widest boundary.

- ejection pattern area for the Sig Sauer P-229 with equivalent ammunition is 8' across and 13' height at the centerline of the ejection pattern area.

- a number of important constraints regarding fired casing locations and target locations must be satisfied by the ejection pattern overlays

- the 23' base of the fired casing area nicely divides into three (3) ejection patterns when each ejection area base is 8' in width, with a minor , reasonable error of about 1'.

- all important constraints regarding fired casing locations and target locations are satisfied by the ejection pattern overlays.

- shooter locations are identified at the apex of each ejection pattern overlay.

- finding first blood and the center of Brown's body at the soot/stippling distance along the trajectory line confirms that these ejection patterns are properly placed in the fired casing area.

- this set of ejection pattern area overlays actually represents a minimum number of ejection patterns.

- Wilson was moving backwards while Brown was charging forward. As Wilson retreated, he continually discharged his firearm in an attempt to stop Brown's attack.

- this movement is explained by the multiple ejection pattern areas inside the fired casing area and by the multiple shooting positions.

- Brown's movement of 21' 7' indicates that Brown was moving quickly, not casually walking forward and surrendering.

- if Wilson were moving forward, the fired casing area would be much smaller. If Wilson were standing over Brown discharging his firearm, the fired casing spread would only cover one (1) ejection pattern area.

Witness Statement Evaluations

Witness statements are all over the place. Several of the most important statements are evaluated in this chapter. One of the witnesses stated that Brown was on his knees. Another witness, Darian Johnson, the percipient witness, claims that Brown turned towards Wilson, took a step forward, and was shot by Wilson. Both of these statements are evaluated.

Witness Statement That Brown On His Knees

One witness was standing in a parking lot on Copper Creek Court along Canfield Drive. According to the witness, "Michael Brown was on his knees." This statement appears in the Grand Jury Testimony transcripts, Volume 16, page 12.

At first blush, the witness seems to imply that Brown was on his knees being executed by Wilson. However, the complete statement by this witness needs to be very carefully considered.

```
12        A    And so by the time I made it to where I
13   could see what was going on, Michael Brown was on
14   his knees.
15        Q    So by the time, so you heard four shots?
16        A    Yes.
17        Q    And then you come down to Coppercreek
18   Court?
19        A    Right.
20        Q    And how far, where do you go?
21        A    I was right in this part right here.
22   (indicating)
23        Q    Near the intersection of Coppercreek?
24        A    Yeah, I went all the way in.
25        Q    And Canfield?
```

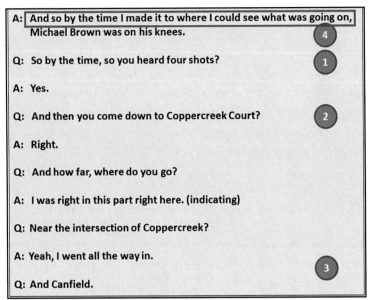

Figure 80: Witness Statement On Brown Kneeling

Appearing in the first line of this statement (and highlighted in red), the witness clearly states "... by the time I made it to where I could see what was going on ...". Clearly, this statement shows that the witness did not see the first part of the event.

Circles to the side of some of the lines indicate the sequence of events experienced by this witness **PRIOR TO SEEING BROWN ON HIS KNEES.**

- Step 1: the witness hears four shots.

- Step 2: the witness comes down from the apartment to Copper Creek Court.

- Step 3: the witness walks down to Canfield Drive.

- Step 4: the witness sees Brown on his knees.

This sequence of events experienced by this witness are easily visualized using Google Earth.

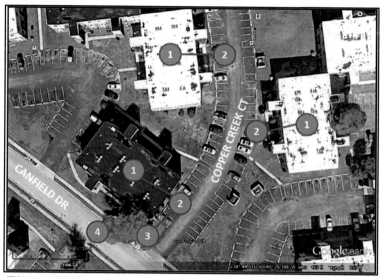

Figure 81: Sequence Of Actions Experienced By Witness

Unfortunately, the witness testimony did not identify the specific residence building. So, any of these three (3) buildings closest to Canfield Drive could have been the residence location of the witness.

In this figure, the sequence of events is indicated from the start of each possible residence location. Position 1 is where the witness heard the 4 shots. Position 3 is where the witness was standing when Brown was observed on his knees. Position 4 is where Brown was actually on his knees (approximately the location of his body).

Regardless of the initial residence location of the witness, this witness arrived at the observation position (Position 3) at the end of the incident. Time had passed between the time the witness heard shots in Position 1, in the residence, and the witness in standing in Position 3, the observation location.

As a result of this time delay, this witness did not see any of the incident that occurred prior to Brown falling on his knees. Shooting had occurred earlier. This witness could not determine if Brown was surrendering with his head bowed or charging.

Given this time delay, the statement that Brown was on his knees has no evidentiary value.

Statement By Dorian Johnson, The Percipient Witness

Dorian Johnson and Michael Brown were together at the time of the incident. Johnson made several statements to the Grand Jury that identified locations of participants during the incident.

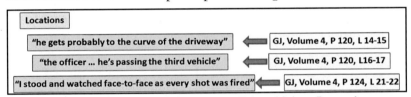

Figure 82: Johnson Statements Identifying Locations

Locations of each of these statements within the Grand Jury testimony documents appear in the figure.

In these statements, Johnson claims that Brown gets to the "curve of the driveway". He locates Wilson as "passing the third vehicle". Johnson himself had fled across Canfield Drive, watching "face to face as every shot was fired".

Unfortunately, no map accompanied the Grand Jury testimony by Johnson. However, some reasonable inferences can be made. "Curve of the driveway" likely refers to the intersection of Copper Creek Court and Canfield Drive. This inference is reasonable because the first blood stains were 26' 7" from this intersection.

A location for the "third vehicle" is not clearly identified in the testimony. But, this location would have been on Canfield Drive, about 8' for so from the location of the first blood stains. this reasonable inference is based on the soot/stippling distance of 8'.

Johnson made several other statements to the Grand Jury that identified the interactions that occurred during the incident.

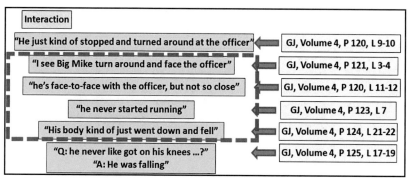

Figure 83: Johnson Statements Identifying Interactions

Again, the locations of these statements within the Grand Jury testimony are provided in the figure above.

In these statements, the key elements of the interaction are provided by Johnson. According to these statements, Brown "turned around at the officer", "never started running", and "just went down and fell". <u>With these statements, Johnson is claiming that Brown turned towards Wilson and was immediately shot by Wilson.</u>

While Johnson was the percipient witness (closest to the incident throughout the complete sequence of actions), these statements cannot be taken at face value, but should be evaluated carefully.

If Brown was shot just after turning towards Wilson, the head shot of wound path one (1) could not have occurred. As previously demonstrated, the bullet trajectory path is at a 90° angle from the wound trajectory path through the top of the head.

Under the conditions characterized by Johnson, the bullet path could only be through the Brown's chest.

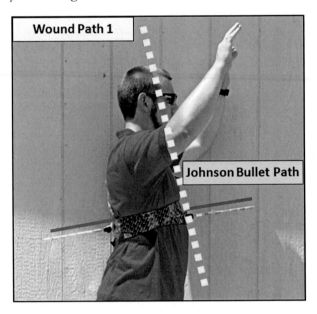

Figure 84: Bullet Path Consistent With Johnson's Statement

In this figure, wound path one (1), through the top of the head, is depicted using a dashed yellow line. A wound path consistent with the statement by Dorian Johnson is shown through the chest area.

This consistent wound path is placed on the body of an actor, using the wound path reconstruction device. A red line is used to emphasize the wound path through the body. Clearly, the wound path through the top of the head does not match with the wound path through the chest area that would have been sustained, if Brown were shot as described by Johnson.

If Brown had been shot by Wilson just after Brown turned, the wound path would have passed straight through the upper body.

During the analysis of the chest wound path, a complete reconstruction of the chest wound path was performed.

Figure 85: Trajectory Path And Wound Path Through Chest

As shown in the figure, the green line depicts the actual chest wound path. Using a red horizontal line, the trajectory bullet path is depicted. Bullet trajectory path is $90°$ to the vertical axis of the body.

Comparison between the chest wound path and the corresponding trajectory path resulted in the following figure.

Figure 86: Chest, Bullet Trajectory Path Angles

If Brown were shot in the chest by Wilson immediately after turning, both the wound path and the bullet trajectory path would be 90° to the vertical axis of the body. However, the actual chest wound path is 40° to the vertical axis of the body, not 90° to the vertical axis of the body.

Johnson's description of the conditions under which Wilson shot Brown simply are not scientifically possible.

Summary And Conclusions

Some key conclusions from this chapter include the following:

- one of the witnesses stated that Brown was on his knees.

- time had passed between the witness hearing shots in the residence and the witness standing at the observation location.

- as a result of this time delay, this witness did not see any of the incident that occurred prior to Brown being on his knees.

- given this time delay, the statement by this witness that Brown was on his knees has no evidentiary value.

- statements made by Dorian Johnson, the percipient witness, infer that Brown turned towards Wilson and was immediately shot by Wilson.

- if Brown had been shot by Wilson just after turning, the wound path would have passed straight through the upper body.

- if Brown were shot in the chest by Wilson immediately after turning, both the wound path and the bullet trajectory path would be 90° to the vertical axis of the body.

- however, the actual chest wound path is 40° to the vertical axis of the body, not 90° to the vertical axis of the body.

- Johnson's description of the conditions under which Wilson shot Brown simply are not scientifically possible.

Independent Medical Examiner Statement

An independent Medical Examiner, Dr. Michael Baden, wrote a separate report detailing his own interpretation of the autopsy results. Dr. Baden's report was included in the Grand Jury evidence released to the public. This report was initially released on August 10, 2014. This interpretation corroborates that Brown was charging at the time of impact of the bullets that created the three wound paths.

Summary Description Of The Wound Paths

In the report by Dr. Baden, the following extract appears.

> Given Mr. Brown's height, his head had to be bent downward with his face near parallel to the ground and the top of his head facing the shooter when the gun was discharged to produce the head and face tracks. In that bent over position the three bullets would have had to have travelled approximately parallel to the ground to produce the head, forehead, and chest perforations only inches apart and then continue in similar trajectories downward and to the right. The exit perforation of the facial wound at the right lower jaw then lines up with the re-entrance wound through the clavicle.

Figure 87: Statement From Independent Examiner Report

Baden's understanding of Brown's body position are highlighted in purple and in red. Based on these clauses, Baden feels that at the time of the impacts, the body of Brown was:

- in a bent over position
- head bent downward
- face near parallel to the ground
- top of head facing the shooter.

213

Just looking at these indicators, the implication seems to be that Dr. Baden thinks that Brown was charging, not surrendering.

Analysis Of Description Of The Wound Paths

Using the indicators from Dr. Baden's statement extract, a reconstruction is performed using the wound path reconstruction device and an actor.

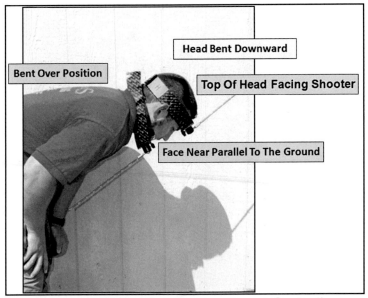

Figure 88: Wound Path Visualization Based On Indicators

In this reconstruction, head wound path two (2) is visualized using the wound path reconstruction device. The body of the actor is place in a position consistent with the indicators from Dr. Baden's statement.

This visualization clearly shows that Dr. Baden is describing Brown in a charging body position when the bullet paths were created. Dr. Baden is **NOT** describing a standing/surrendering body position.

214

Based on the indicators and the visualization, Dr. Baden's statement clearly corroborates the theory of the incident that Brown was charging at Wilson.

Summary And Conclusions

Important conclusions from this chapter include the following:

- According to the Independent Medical Examiner's Report, the body of Brown was in a bent over position, head bent downward, face near parallel to the ground, and top of the head facing the shooter.

- Dr. Baden is describing Brown in a charging body position when the bullet paths were created.

- Dr. Baden's statement clearly corroborates the theory of the incident that Brown was charging at Wilson.

Level Of Danger To Wilson

Systematic and scientific analyses to this point have clearly established that Brown was charging Officer Wilson with officer Wilson retreating. Previous analyses that established this theory of the incident include:

- head wound path one (1), through the top of the head and vertically downward through the head, was the wound path that terminated the life of Brown.

- since the line of sight, the trajectory bullet path and the wound bullet path perfectly coincide for head wound path one (1) when Brown is charging, Brown charging is scientifically correct and is exactly what happened.

- Brown charging is the only scientifically correct theory of the incident because this theory was the only theory in which the line of sight, the trajectory bullet path and the wound bullet path perfectly coincide for head wound path one (1) .

- Wilson was retreating while shooting. This movement is explained by the multiple ejection pattern areas inside the fired casing area and by the resultant multiple shooting positions.

- since the chest wound path angle and the bullet trajectory path angle relative to the vertical axis of the body do not match, Brown could not have been standing during the time at which the chest wound path was created.

- Dr. Michael Baden, independent Medical Examiner, describes Brown in a charging body position when the bullet paths were created

In this chapter, an analysis is performed that clearly identifies the level of danger that Wilson faced by a charging Brown. Both scientific and anecdotal results are provided.

Level Of Force Analysis

Everyone knows two truths about the use of force. At impact, a force can cause damage. Moreover, the greater the force, the greater the damage.

In the scientific foundation section, examples were provided that demonstrated the amount of force at impact caused by two different bullets. Here, the amount of force is calculated when a charging Brown impacts Wilson.

Not surprisingly, when a 289 pound object (Brown) impacts another object, this amounts to a very large application of force.

Contained in the table below are the force calculations for impact by a charging Brown. For comparison, impact force calculations for a 308 Winchester bullet are included in the table.

Object	Bullet Weight (grains)	Impact Weight (lbs)	Impact Velocity (ft/sec)	Momentum At Impact (lb ft/sec)	Force At Impact (lb ft/sec^2)	Force At Impact (Newtons)
Brown	--	289	8.8(*)	2543	1271500	175784
308 Win	168	.024	2640	63	31500	4354

Table 14: Brown Charging Impact Force Calculations

Several parameters are used in these calculations. Charging speed is assumed to be at the speed of a person running a mile in 10 minutes. Ultimately, this translates into a velocity of 8.8 feet/second. In fact, this velocity may be somewhat low, giving a conservative estimate for Brown's force at impact.

Impact duration, necessary for translation from momentum into force, is assumed to be 2 milliseconds. Maximum force at impact occurs within this time period. After this time period, impulse response (pushback by the impacted object), reduces the momentum of the bullet and thus reduces the force.

These calculations are generally used in a comparative manner. Force at impact by one object is compared to force at impact by another object.

As the first comparison, consider the force at impact of a 308 Winchester bullet. Brown's force at impact would be 40 times greater than the impact of a 308 bullet. Given that the 308 bullet can cause death, impact by a charging Brown has to at least cause a lot of damage to Wilson's body.

Another comparison is to force at impact of Brown charging with force of impact of a 40 pound rock. Using the mathematical formulas from Appendix E, the impact force of a charging Brown is equivalent to the impact force of a 40 pound rock swung at 40 miles/hour.

With this level of force at impact, if a charging Brown had impacted, some damage and potentially the death of Wilson would have occurred.

Anecdotal Corroboration Of Force Analysis

Examples of impact damage from a charging person are readily available. An anecdotal example of charging damage at impact is from the 1964 American Football League (AFL) championship game. This impact is identified in the news media as "The Hit Heard Round The World".

A frame from the video showing the bodies at impact appears below.

Table 15: The Hit Heard Round The World

In this game, Mike Stratton knocked into Keith Lincoln. A charging Stratton is on the left. Impacted Lincoln is on the right. After this impact, Lincoln had three (3) broken ribs.

Stratton was 6' 3" weighing 224 pounds. Lincoln was 6' 1", weighing 215 pounds. This impact is a clear example of an impact of a larger, heavier person against a somewhat smaller, heavier person, very similar to the situation of Brown charging at Wilson.

Lincoln experienced body damage as a result of the impact by charging Stratton.

This impact was delivered with such force that Lincoln is actually doubled over at the point of impact. That result alone demonstrates that the impact delivered a lot of force.

A basic similarity exists between this situation and the situation in which Brown was charging Wilson. A larger, heavier person was charging a somewhat smaller, heavier person. As a result of this basic similarity, this example qualifies as a real-world corroboration of the physics predictions in the previous chapter.

However, significant differences exist that indicate that the damage to Wilson would have been far greater.

Brown was 289 pounds while Wilson was 210 pounds -- a significant weight difference. <u>Greater charging weight yields greater impact force, causing greater damage</u>.

Lincoln was wearing protective gear specifically designed to lessen the force of impact. Wilson had no such protective gear. <u>Lesser protection yields greater impact force, causing greater damage.</u>

Summary And Conclusions

Important conclusions from this chapter include the following:

- Brown's force at impact would be 40 times greater than the impact of a 308 bullet.

- Brown's force at impact is equivalent to the impact force of a 40 pound rock swung at 40 miles/hour.

- if a charging Brown had impacted, some damage and potentially the death of Wilson would have occurred.

Final, Resting Body Position Analysis

In the Investigation Report, the resting position of the body is characterized. This body position provides some insight into the position of the body just prior to the resting position of the body.

Visualization with an actor is used to evaluate two possible theories of the incident. One theory is that Brown is standing/surrendering just prior to the resting position of the body. Another theory is that Brown is charging just prior to the resting position of the body.

Emphasis is placed upon the __transition__ from the position prior to the resting place to the final, resting position of the body. Dynamics of the transition are visually captured and explained.

Subsequent to the visual analysis, an anecdotal example from a real shooting incident is provided that corroborates the visual analysis of the theory of the incident that has Brown standing/surrendering.

Resting Position Of Brown's Body

In the Police Report, the final position of Brown's body is described.

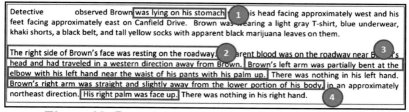

Figure 89: Description Of Brown's Body Position

This extract is from Police Report 14-43984, page 7. Numbered circles are used to indicate key locations of the body elements.

An actor was placed into a position that reflects the body element locations identified in the above extract.

Figure 90: Visualization Of Body Resting Position

Each of the numbered circles from the extract appears in the visualization, as follows:

> 1: body was lying on the stomach
> 2: right side of face was on the roadway
> 3: left arm partially bent, hand near waist, palm up
> 4: right arm straight, right palm up.

Most importantly, the body was lying on its stomach with the palms upward.

The primary goal of the visual analysis is to determine which of the prior body positions would result in a final resting position with these two features -- standing/surrendering or charging.

Visual Analysis Of Brown Standing/Surrendering

Brown begins this visual analysis with his body in a standing/surrendering body position. His upper body is slightly forward with his hands in the air in a surrender position.

Figure 91: Brown In A Standing/ Surrendering Position

In this position, the weight of Brown's posterior is somewhat to the rear of the centerline of the body. This positioning is necessary to insure balance of the whole body. However, any potential imbalance will be to the rearward.

Upon impact, the legs tend to collapse somewhat in shock.

Figure 92: Brown's Leg Collapsing On Bullet Impact

When the legs collapse in shock, the weight of the posterior draws the posterior downward.

Since this weight is to the rear of the centerline of the body, the body is also pulled to the rear.

Figure 93: Weight Of Body Falling And To Rear

As the body falls to the rear and downward, the shoulders move to the rear. Also, as the body is falling, the hands start coming down from surrender position.

When the hands start coming down, the palms just naturally rotate downward from the surrender position.

The upper body keeps falling to the rear, since the shoulders are angled backwards from the center line of the body. As the shoulders fall, the hands remain in the palm down orientation.

Ultimately, the body comes to a final resting position.

Figure 94: Resting Position From Surrender Start Position

Due to the posterior starting off centerline controlling the weight imbalance to the rearward, the body comes to a final resting position as shown above. The back is on the ground. Palms are face down.

A final, resting position with back on the ground and with palms down **DOES NOT** match the final, resting position of Brown's body as reported in the Incident Report.

This final, resting position of Brown's body does not corroborate the theory of the incident that Brown was standing/surrendering.

Visual Analysis Of Brown Charging

Brown's starting position when charging is different from the starting position prior to surrendering. In this starting position, the weight of the upper body is forward, dominating the balanced position of Brown's body.

Figure 95: Brown's Body Starting Position When Charging

When charging, the upper body is canted forward and the arms are usually bent at the elbows with the forearms level to the ground. Because the body is in rapid forward motion, the body possesses a fairly high level of forward momentum.

Upon impact, the legs still seem to collapse due to the shock on the body systems.

Figure 96: Brown's Body Falling Forward And Down

As the legs collapse, the forward momentum of the body in motion causes an imbalance due to the upper body position leaning forward.

Figure 97: Body Dropping Forward Towards Ground

The body pitches forward due to momentum and downward due to gravity. As the body pitches forward and downward, the body drops to the knees. While pitching forward, the arms are thrown out to the rear. Throwing the arms to the rear results in the palms landing face up.

Figure 98: Resting Position From Charging Start Position

Due to the forward upper body controlling the weight imbalance to the forward and the combined forward, downward movement, the body comes to a final resting position as shown above. The stomach is on the ground. Palms are face up.

A final, resting position with stomach on the ground and with palms up **DOES** match the final, resting position of Brown's body as reported in the Incident Report.

This final, resting position of Brown's body does corroborate the theory of the incident that Brown was charging.

Anecdotal Corroboration, Brown Standing/Surrendering

A recent shooting incident reviewed by the author was captured on surveillance video. In this video, the victim was pursuing the shooter. While the victim was pursuing, the victim was trotting, not charging. Body position of the trotting victim during pursuit was a standing up position.

Clearly, this video represents an effective anecdotal characterization of the body behavior after impact when the victim is standing.

Video frames immediately before and after bullet impact are shown, These frames of video corroborate the visual reconstruction of the standing/surrendering analysis previously described.

These video frames were extracted using Amped 5 software. This software package is used by many law enforcement agencies, including the LAPD Crime Lab.

Body position of the victim just prior to impact is shown in the video frame below.

Figure 99: Victim In Pursuit While Trotting

In this video frame, the victim is in the center of the frame, next to the double line.

This frame show the victim just before bullet impact. The victim appears to be standing almost vertical.

Figure 100: Victim Falling Almost Straight Down

This frame show the victim just after bullet impact. The victim has fallen almost straight down. This victim is sitting on his posterior.

This anecdotal evidence corroborates the visual reconstruction that shows Brown falling almost straight down and falling backwards on his posterior if he had been standing/surrendering.

Summary And Conclusions

Important points presented in this chapter include the following:

- the body was lying on its stomach with the palms upward.

- standing/surrendering starts with a potential weight imbalance to the rearward.

- this potential rearward imbalance results in a final resting position with the back on the ground and palms face down.

- This final, resting position of Brown's body does not corroborate the theory of the incident that Brown was standing/surrendering.

- charging starts with a potential weight imbalance to the forward.

- this potential forward imbalance results in a final resting position with the stomach on the ground and palms face up.

- This final, resting position of Brown's body does corroborate the theory of the incident that Brown was charging.

Words Of Warning

WHILE DETAILED AND THOROUGH, THIS BOOK DOES HAVE LIMITATIONS.

Many of the approaches will apply to many shooting incidents. However, some of these approaches will not apply to some incidents. Furthermore, some incidents often require additional approaches not even covered in this book.

A simple reason exists for these statements. Shooting incidents encompass a broad range of issues, not all of which are represented in this book.

Here is a list of some of the other issues that might appear in a shooting incident, that might require additional :

- line of sight between an alleged shooter and an alleged target
- impact on terminal materials such as wood, stone, cinder blocks
- multiple reverse trajectories
- drive-by shooting from a vehicle
- shooting from the passenger side across the driver
- shooting up or down a hillside
- eyewitness claims
- sound analysis
- video analysis

Additionally, multiple techniques may be used to evaluate a given issue in a shooting incident. Examples of these different approaches to evaluate a given issue appear throughout this book.

235

For head wound path evaluation, trajectory bullet path and wound bullet path difference is used to evaluate alternate theories of the incident. When the chest wound path was evaluated, the trajectory bullet path and wound bullet path angles were computed relative to the vertical axis of the body.

Both approaches are valid. Either approach could be used to evaluate alternate theories of the incident. Either approach would lead to the exact same conclusions.

A different approach was used for head wound path evaluation and chest wound path evaluation simply to show that the approaches are interchangeable.

When performing a shooting incident reconstruction, use an approach that is appropriate for the specific evidence and data collected in the incident. JUST MAKE SURE THAT THE APPROACH USED IS SYSTEMATIC (COMBINES MULTIPLE SOURCES OF EVIDENCE) AND SCIENTIFIC (BASED ON MATH AND PHYSICS).

Several popular books on shooting incident reconstruction emphasize scientific methods for data collection. Data collection is useful and certainly is an important element of shooting incident reconstruction. HOWEVER, DATA COLLECTION BY ITSELF SIMPLY DOES NOT PROVE ANYTHING AT ALL ABOUT THE INCIDENT.

An emphasis strictly on the scientific collection of data is misleading. Collected data provides a foundation for a systematic reconstruction and is only one aspect of the incident. Unfortunately, the emphasis on data collection often leads to collection of wrong or useless data. Determining the data to collect depends upon the theory of the incident that is being evaluated using that data. Without understanding the need for the data and the theory being evaluated, the data that is collected is often a waste of time and money, contributing nothing at all to evaluating a specific theory of the incident. Worse yet, emphasis on data collection often leads to near sightedness. Data is collected and presented as proof that the accused performed the alleged shooting incident according to a specific theory of the incident.

A simple example should make this issue fairly clear. In one case, the prosecution claimed that a younger man was chasing an older man and shooting at the older man. the older man was wounded was alive and well. In an interview, the accused claimed that a struggle for the pistol resulted in multiple unintended discharges.

A huge difference exists between these two theories of the incident. The charge for the chasing theory was attempted murder. Attempted voluntary manslaughter was the charge for the struggle theory.

Since the event took place inside a home, the crime scene team collected data. The crime scene team characterized each of the bullet impacts. Each impact was described by a height above the floor, left/right angle, and up/down angle. A report summarizing this data was presented by the prosecution as proof that the younger was chasing the older man and shooting at the older man.

Unfortunately, this data proves nothing about the actions of either the younger man or the older man. This data simply describes the final segment of each trajectory. Thus, this data is not useful to distinguish between the chasing and the struggle theory.

A reverse trajectory was performed upon each of the represented final segments in the collected impact data. When represented visually, the combined reversed trajectories revealed some clear patterns which were used to evaluate two theories of the incident - the chasing theory and the struggle theory.

- Multiple reverse trajectories intersected. Intersection means that all of the intersecting trajectories were discharged from the intersection location.

- Intersecting trajectories exhibited impacts across a wide distance and on both sides of the room.

A visualization was accomplished with actors. This visualization enabled an evaluation of the two alternate theories.

Using actors to visualize, as demonstrated earlier, the struggle theory was shown to be scientifically possible. During the struggle, the victim was pushing and pulling the firearm back and forth. This pushing and pulling motion led to the impacts across a wide distance and on both sides of the room.

A similar visualization was performed based upon the chasing theory. This visualization revealed that the chasing theory was not scientifically possible. If the younger man were chasing the older man, the bullet impacts would always be spread across a fairly narrow distance and generally on the same wall, not on walls on both sides of the room.

Moreover, one of the impacts was the result of a trajectory into a blind corner with no way out for the victim. If the younger man had chased the older man into this corner, and was up close, the older man would be dead. But, the older man was wounded but alive and well.

EMPHASIS ON DATA COLLECTION BY THE CRIME LAB DID NOT PROVE ANYTHING ABOUT EITHER THEORY OF THE INCIDENT. Systematic (combining the data) and scientific (using straight, flat trajectories and intersecting lines) analysis was necessary to really investigate the scientific possibility of each alternate theory of the incident.

Concluding Remarks

Officer Darren Wilson has been charged with the murder of Michael Brown on August 9, 2014. You have been selected to be a member of the jury on this case.

A prosecutor presents his case. After presenting his case, the prosecution rests.

A defense attorney calls me to the stand. I testify that Michael Brown was charging. I also testify that Officer Darren Wilson was retreating, defending himself in fear of his life. I explain my reasons using a series of slides extracted from this book. Then, the defense rests, presenting only my systematic and scientific analysis.

Your decision now is whether or not Wilson is guilty as charged.

Read my one page summary --
                 Ferguson MO: In A Nutshell.

Then, read my multi-paged, detailed summary --
A Summary Of The Systematic, Scientific Analysis.

Now, take two weeks and read this complete book, carefully reviewing my rationale for each of the conclusions that I make.

How would you vote?

Bruce Krell, PhD

241

Appendices

Appendix A

A: Summary Of Most Destructive Wounds, Metric Units

Number	Entrance	Direction	Exit
1	Vertex of the scalp 20 cm above right auditory meatus Midline of vertex of head	Downward, rightward	At rest within soft tissue of right lateral face
2, 3	Central forehead 7 cm above right auditory meatus 2 cm right of anterior midline of head	Downward, slightly backward and rightward	Right jaw 5.5 cm below right auditory meatus 11 cm right of anterior midline of head
4	Upper right chest 16 cm below right auditory meatus 9 cm right of anterior midline of chest	Slightly downward, Slightly backward	At rest Within soft tissue of right chest (posterier 3rd right intercostal space)
5	Lateral right chest 20 cm below right auditory meatus 22 cm right of anterior midline of chest	Downward, backward	At rest Within soft tissue of lateral right back (fractures 8th rib)

Appendix B

B: Witness Statement Summary, Grand Jury Testimony

Category	Witness	Statement	Source
Charging	Darren Wilson	"like he was going to run right through me"	GJ Vol 5 P 229
	Witness walking towards vehicle	"When he charged once more"	GJ Vol 6 P 167
	Witness sitting in van	"started charging towards the officer"	GJ Vol 18 P 27
	Witness driving through complex	"I thought he was trying to charge him"	GJ Vol 11 P 181
Walking Back	Witness travelling through complex in van	"it wasn't fast enough to be a charge"	GJ Vol 12 P 44
	Witness on patio of apartment	"casually walking"	GJ Vol 11 P 151
	Witness sitting in van with family	"he picked up a little bit of speed"	GJ Vol 23 P 137
	Witness in 2nd floor apartment, looking through window, then on balcony	"taking two small steps"	GJ Vol 7 P 21

Category	Witness	Statement	Source
Turned Around	Witness stopped in vehicle along Canfield	"turn around facing the officer"	GJ Vol 12 P 120
	Witness sitting in car parked in complex	"he was turned around"	GJ Vol 7 P 102
	Witness looking out window of her apartment	"I saw him turn to his right"	GJ Vol 9 P 22
	Witness standing in grass about 20 feet from shooting	"turned around"	GJ Vol 6 P 252
	Witness on exterior stairs of apartment complex	"He turned around"	GJ Vol 10 P 41
Falling	Witness standing in a parking lot on Copper Creek Court along Canfield Drive	"Michael Brown was on his knees"	GJ Vol 16 P 12
	Witness doing maintenance work at the complex	"he was just catching his balance"	GJ Vol 12 P 240

Category	Witness	Statement	Source
Surrender	Witness stopped in her vehicle on Canfield	"kept saying, I got, my hands is up"	GJ Vol 17 P 212
	Witness standing on porch outside of second floor apartment	"he was walking in a demeanor as I give up"	GJ Vol 9 P 98
	Witness doing maintenance work at complex	"okay, okay, okay, hands up"	GJ Vol 13 P 219
	Witness walking along sidewalk on Canfield	"he put his arms about shoulder length and just stopped"	GJ Vol 17 P 25
	Witness on apartment porch	"Mike Brown with his arms up"	GJ Vol 16 P 60
	Witness standing on porch of apartment	"he was giving up"	GJ Vol 8 P 148
	Witness sitting in vehicle stopped along Canfield	"he was not close at all to him"	GJ Vol 7 P 167

Note To The Reader About The Equations

In the next several appendices, a series of equations are presented that represent the theoretical physics basis for the scientific reconstruction process.

Each of the series may appear to be nothing more than a list of equations that were copied and pasted from the source. **If this is your thinking, you are quite wrong.**

The trajectory physics equations were implemented **BY THIS AUTHOR** in a computer program named MOAMaster^{tm}. And, the equations of motion were implemented, again, **BY THIS AUTHOR**, in a computer program named GSMaster^{tm}. Both of these programs have been utilized over the years. Predictions generated by both of these programs have been validated through extensive testing with real firearms and cartridges, as explained in the text.

In order to implement these equations in computer programs, the equations had to be updated. Symbols used in the original text were inconsistent, because the original equations were spread all over various parts of the text. Since the equations were spread all over, the equations also had to be organized in the proper sequence so that the outputs from the prior equations would be available when necessary for a subsequent equation. The equations you see in the following appendices use the consistent symbols and the correct sequencing for implementation in a computer program.

Moreover, you see every variable, constant, parameter, and component clearly defined with the units of measurement specified. Published books and articles are often sloppy in the definition of the variables or specification of measurement units, assuming that the reader is knowledgeable. Sometimes, the variables, etc., are defined in one location of the published source but not replicated in the actual location of the equations.

Rewriting the equations with consistent notation, determining the proper sequencing of the equations, defining every variable, etc., writing the program, and testing the predictions of the program demonstrates that the person performing these tasks possesses a fundamental and detailed understanding of the equations themselves.

These equations, definitions, and units of measurement are available because the author actually understands the underlying laws of physics involved. So, **these equations represent the scientific knowledge of the author, not just a copy and paste of the equations.**

Appendix C

C: Trajectory Equations of Motion

Coordinate System

$x =$ *downrange distance along the line of sight (feet)*
$y =$ *height above or below line of sight (feet)*
$z =$ *cross range distance orthogonal to line of sight (feet)*

Kinematic Variables

$v_x =$ *downrange velocity along the line of sight* $(\frac{feet}{sec})$

$v_y =$ *vertical velocity above or below line of sight* $(\frac{feet}{sec})$

$v_z =$ *cross range velocity orthogonal to line of sight* $(\frac{feet}{sec})$

$\dot{v}_x =$ *downrange acceleration along the line of sight* $(\frac{feet}{sec^2})$

$\dot{v}_y =$ *vertical acceleration above or below line of sight* $(\frac{feet}{sec^2})$

$\dot{v}_z =$ *cross range acceleration orthogonal to line of sight* $(\frac{feet}{sec^2})$

$w_x =$ *downrange wind speed along the line of sight* $(\frac{feet}{sec})$

$w_y =$ *vertical wind speed above or below line of sight* $(\frac{feet}{sec})$

$w_z =$ *cross range wind speed orthogonal to line of sight* $(\frac{feet}{sec})$

Equations of Motion

$$\dot{v}_x = -E(v_x - w_x)$$
$$\dot{v}_y = -E(v_y - w_y) - g$$
$$\dot{v}_z = -E(v_z - w_z)$$

$$E = (e^{-hY_a})\rho^* v \left(\frac{d^{*2}}{m^*}\right) K_D \left(\frac{v/\sqrt{\frac{\theta}{\theta_B(0)}}}{v_B(0)}\right) / C$$

$$v = \sqrt{(v_x - w_x)^2 + (v_y - w_y)^2 + (v_z - w_z)^2}$$

Constants

g = acceleration due to gravity = 32.15 ft/sec^2

h = air density decay constant = 3.158 e^{-5} /foot

ρ^* = standard air density at sea level = .075126 lbs/ft^3

d^* = diameter of standard projectile = 1 in

m^* = mass of standard projectile = 1 lb

$\Theta_B(0)$ = standard absolute temperature at sea level = 59°F

$v_B(0)$ = speed of sound at sea level = 1120 ft/sec

Parameters

Y_a = altitude of start location above sea level, feet

Θ = absolute temperature at start location, °F

C = ballistic coefficient , dimensionless

$K_D(Mach)$ = drag coefficient, dimensionless

Initial Values

$x_0 = 0.0$, $y_0 = 0.0$, $z_0 = 0.0$

$v_x = v_0$, $v_y = 0.0$, $v_z = 0.0$

$w_x = 0.0$, $w_y = 0.0$, $w_z = 0.0$

Inputs

C = ballistic coefficient , dimensionless

v_0 = muzzle velocity, feet/sec

Extracted and Combined From

Exterior Ballistics

EJ McShane, JL Kelley, FV Reno

University of Denver Press, ©1953

Appendix D

D: Gyroscopic Equations of Stability

Inputs

W = weight of bullet, grains

L = total length of bullet, inches

L_m = total length of metallic portion of bullet, inches

[equals L for non − plastic tipped bullets]

V = velocity of bullet, ft/sec (at any time during trajectory)

D = diameter of bullet, inches

T = barrel twist, turns/in

P = air pressure, in Hg

T_f = air temperature, °F

Equations of Stability

$$T_A = \frac{T}{D}$$

$$L_A = \frac{L}{D}$$

$$L_M = \frac{L_m}{D}$$

$$A = \frac{T_f + 460}{T_s + 460} \left(\frac{P_s}{P}\right)$$

$$GS_v = \left(\frac{(30\,W)}{T_A^2\,D^3 L_A\,(1 + L_M^2)}\right) \left(\frac{V}{2800}\right)^{1/3} A$$

253

Components

T_A = barrel twist, inches/turn

L_A = total length of bullet, calibers

L_M = total length of metal portion length of bullet, calibers

[equals L_A for non − plastic tipped bullets]

A = correction for temperature, pressure, unitless

GS_v = gyroscopic stability factor, unitless

Parameters

P_S = standard atmosphere, air pressure, 29.92 in Hg

T_S = standard atmosphere, air temperature, 59 °F

Extracted and Combined From

"A Stability Formula For Plastic Tipped Bullets"
Michael Courtney and Donald Miller
Precision Shooting, January, 2012

Appendix E

E: Momentum and Force Equations

Inputs

m = bullet weight(grains) / 7000 (grains/lb)
v_i = velocity at impact (ft/sec)
v_0 = velocity at muzzle (ft/sec)
t = time after impact (sec)

a = acceleration after impact (ft/ sec^2)

Components

P = momentum (lb ft/sec)
F = force (lb ft/sec^2)

Momentum

$$P = m * v_i \text{ (at impact)}$$
$$P = m * v_0 \text{ (at muzzle)}$$

Force

$$F = m \times a = m * v_i / t$$

<u>Extracted From</u>

ANY HIGH SCHOOL PHYSICS TEXTBOOK

Appendix F

F: Systematic Analysis Procedure Summary

A systematic approach is based upon principles, procedures, and techniques. Every procedure involves inputs, an ordered sequence of steps to follow, outputs, and, when appropriate, evaluation rules.

In the body of the text, several procedures are enumerated. However, the elements of the procedure are spread over many pages. As an aid to practitioners of the systematic approach utilized in this book, a centralized summary of the key procedures is provided, explicitly identifying the elements of the procedure.

SOME OF THESE PROCEDURES MAY NEED TO BE MODIFIED OR ADJUSTED FOR YOUR SPECIFIC SHOOTING INCIDENT.

Performing A Shooting Incident Reconstruction

Inputs

- location of the incident

- summary of sequence of events

- physical characteristics of the participants

- map and locations of fired casings and physical evidence

- firearms and ammunition involved

- wounds and wound paths

- police investigation reports

- statements of percipient witnesses

- statements of other witnesses

Steps
- gather the relevant physical evidence, as previously outlined

- identify multiple theories of the incident

- identify and gather additional data as needed, such as ejection patterns, soot/stippling distance

- evaluate the multiple theories of the incident using the physical evidence, the additional data, visualizations, and science

- identify the specific theory of the incident justified by the physical evidence, the additional data, visualizations, and science

- rebut the other theories of the incident justified by the physical evidence, the additional data, visualization, and science

- use witness statements to confirm the specific theory of the incident using the physical evidence, the additional data, visualizations, and science

- rebut witness statements using the physical evidence, the additional data, visualizations, and science

258

- corroborate the selected theory of the incident by an analysis of the physics of impact and the final body position

Outputs

- visualizations of multiple theories of the incident

- fired casing areas with ejection pattern overlays

- one or more theories of the incident that are scientifically possible

Evaluating Theories Using Visualization - Head Wounds

Inputs
- relative height differences **(actual evidence)**,
- the bullet paths through the body **(actual evidence)**,
- the flat and straight bullet trajectory through the air **(science)**,
- the soot and stippling distance results **(experimental data)**
- alternate theories of the incident

Steps

- locate the entry wound on the outside of the body of the victim

- if the wound path possesses a bullet resting place, locate the nearest location to the bullet resting place on the outside of the body of the victim

- if the wound path possesses an exit wound, locate the exit wound on the body of the victim

- place a wound reconstruction device with a rotating head over the marked location of the entrance wound

- place another wound reconstruction device with a rotating head over the marked location of the resting place or the exit wound
- align the two dowels for entrance and exit/resting place devices so that the dowels represent a straight line through the body
- place the victim body in the position indicated by the alternate theory of the incident
- establish the trajectory bullet path through the air to the entrance wound location using the PVC pipes and the tripods
- place the shooter body at the opposite end of the trajectory bullet path through the air from the victim body
- place the shooter hand holding a pistol at the start of the trajectory bullet path
- photograph the whole visualization including shooter, victim, bullet path through the air, and wound path through the body
- measure the angular difference between the trajectory bullet path and the wound bullet path
- note the location of the pistol hand relative to the accurate shooting position.

Outputs
- visualization of the body position, trajectory path, wound path
- difference angle between trajectory path, wound path

- if the difference angle is greater than zero (0), then the theory of the incident represented by the body position is not scientifically possible

- if the difference angle is equal to zero (0), then the theory of the incident represented by the body position is scientifically possible

Alternate Theories Using Visualization -- Chest Wounds

Inputs
- relative height differences **(actual evidence)**,
- the bullet paths through the body **(actual evidence)**,
- the flat and straight bullet trajectory through the air **(science)**,
- the soot and stippling distance results **(experimental data)**
- alternate theories of the incident

Steps
- locate and mark the entry wound on the outside of the body of the victim

- if the wound path possesses a bullet resting place, locate and mark the nearest location to the bullet resting place on the outside of the body of the victim

- if the wound path possesses an exit wound, locate and mark the exit wound on the body of the victim

- place a wound reconstruction device with a rotating head over the marked location of the entrance wound

- place another wound reconstruction device with a rotating head over the marked location of the resting place or the exit wound
- align the two dowels for entrance and exit/resting place devices so that the dowels represent a straight line through the body
- place the victim body in the position indicated by the alternate theory of the incident
- establish the trajectory bullet path through the air to the entrance wound location using the PVC pipes and the tripods
- place the shooter body at the opposite end of the trajectory bullet path through the air from the victim body
- place the shooter hand holding a pistol at the start of the trajectory bullet path
- photograph the whole visualization including shooter, victim, bullet path through the air, and wound path through the body
- measure the angle between the vertical axis of the body and the trajectory bullet path
- measure the angle between the vertical axis of the body and the wound bullet path
- note the location of the pistol hand relative to the accurate shooting position.

Outputs
- visualization of the body position, trajectory path, wound path

- trajectory path angle = angle between the vertical axis of the body and the trajectory path

- wound path angle = angle between the vertical axis of the body and the wound path

Evaluation Rules
- if the trajectory path angle is not equal the wound path angle, then the theory of the incident represented by the body position is not scientifically possible

- if the trajectory path angle is equal the wound path angle, then the theory of the incident represented by the body position is scientifically possible

Fired Casing Analysis And Ejection Pattern Overlay

Inputs
- physical location of the fired casings **(actual evidence),**
- first blood and final body locations **(actual evidence),**
- the flat and straight bullet trajectory through the air **(science),**
- combined trajectory, ejection pattern**(systematic integration),**
- the soot and stippling distance results **(experimental data)**
- ejection pattern of Officer Wilson's pistol **(experimental data)**

Steps
- place the ejection areas onto the fired casing area so that the bases of the areas completely cover the widest boundary of the fired casing area and so that none of the areas overlap each other

- for each ejection area,

> identify the ejection centerline of each ejection area

> draw the trajectory line at the ejection angle from the apex of the centerline

> mark the shooting distance along the trajectory line

Outputs
- fired casing area ejection pattern overlay diagram

Evaluation Rules
- if a single ejection pattern fits into the fired casing area, the shooter was standing still

- if multiple ejection patterns fit into the fired casing area, the shooter was moving

- if two (2) to three (3) ejection patterns fit into the fired casing area, the shooter was moving forwards

- if at least three (3) ejection patterns fit into the fired casing area, the shooter was moving backwards